DEFEND
WITH YOUR LIFE

SQUEEZE
BOOKS

Terence Reese & Eddie Kantar

British Library Cataloguing in Publication Data
Reese, Terence
Defend with your life.
1. Contract bridge
I. Title II. Kantar, Eddie
795.41'5 GV 1282.3

ISBN-10: 1-58776-146-7
ISBN-13: 978-1-58776-146-1

10 9 8 7 6 5 4 3 2

Printed in the United States of America

SQueeZe Books is an imprint of Vivisphere Publishing

VIVISPHERE
PUBLISHING
A division of NetPub Corporation
675 Dutchess Turnpike, Poughkeepsie, NY 12603
www.vivisphere.com   (800) 724-1100

Foreword

For many years 'Kantar for the Defense' has been a greatly admired feature of the Bridge World: testing problems tautly described, exactly analysed. Having begun a magazine feature myself, called 'Defend With Your Life', I suggested to Eddie that we essay a joint venture. We put our heads together, and this book is the result.

Let it be said at once that most of the problems are difficult. In the foreword to another book I commented that the test of a good problem was that the reader should say to himself, 'I ought to have got that; next time, I will.' About some of the problems in this book I think players are more likely to say, 'If I could make a play like that at the table, I'd be really proud.'

But this doesn't mean that the problems are impractical. All contain a principle that can be applied to similar situations.. We have good reason, therefore, to urge the reader not to give up easily. Don't think, 'There's no good answer to this', and impatiently turn the page. If you work at the problems in the right way, assembling all the information available, you will find that your notions of defensive play will be transformed.

Apart from one or two at the beginning and end, the problems are in completely random order and the titles are just a point of reference. It is a book for 'dipping in', not for reading straight through. A couple of problems each night will keep you awake or send you to sleep-one or the other!

In any English-American venture there is the inevitable question of style and spelling. Since I have put most of the words together, though often following Eddie's original text, the style is mostly English; but where different usages are equally comprehensible (such as neither side vulnerable in place of love all), I have inclined to American practice-sorry, practise.

TERENCE REESE

Intro

Imagine my surprise when my friend Ron Garber called and asked if I would like to resurrect "Defend With Your Life", a book I had coauthored with Terence Reese almost 25 years ago. A book that had gone out of print. I jumped at the chance. No author likes to see one of his books go out of print (the only thing worse is seeing one of your books on the discount pile at a book store). Besides, this was (is) a good book with great problems.

While checking and doublechecking with Ron looking for possible errors that might have been overlooked along with modernizing the bidding a bit, plus changing a few words like "tele" to television, I decided to see how many of my own problems I could get. I missed a couple! O.K three.

As Terence Reese said in the introduction he wrote to the "first edition", these are challenging problems and fun to struggle with. My feeling is that anybody who gets 60% or more correct has the right to consider him or herself an expert defender.

EDDIE KANTAR

Publisher's Note

I discovered Terence Reese and met Eddie Kantar at about the same time (1960). Since then I have gaped at Reese and laughed with Kantar.

About twenty years ago (1981) the two most popular bridge authors of all time teamed up for the first and only time. That book was printed in hard cover in England and was practically unseen on the western shores of the Atlantic.

Enter on-demand publishing. Not only have we brought the book back (more affordably), we gave Eddie a chance to express himself. The original featured his problems and Reese's commentary. This edition has a delicate balance of Reese's sardonic Etonian wit and Kantar's self deprecating Venice Beach style.

Whether you are an expert or aspiring to be one, this book should both improve your defense and entertain you.

Ron Garber
for SQueeZe Books

Contents

1. The Beginning, the Middle-and Almost the End

Dealer South   Both sides vulnerable

              ♠ J 5
              ♡ K J 8 7
              ◇ 9 4 2
              ♣ A K 10 6

    ♠ Q 9 8 6 3
    ♡ 5
    ◇ K 10 6 3
    ♣ 9 4 2

South	West	North	East
1♡	Pass	4♣	Pass
6♡	Pass	Pass	Pass

North-South are playing a variation of the Swiss convention in which the response of four clubs indicates opening bid values, at least four trump, and no singleton. Most players nowadays use the Jacoby 2NT response to show this type of hand.

Sitting West, and playing with an unfamiliar partner, you lead the 6 of spades, which is covered by the 5, king and ace. South plays three rounds of clubs, ruffing, draws two trumps, and ruffs the fourth club. Then he exits with the 10 of spades; queen from you, jack from dummy, 2 from partner. What do you play now?

Answer 1

```
              ♠ J 5
              ♡ K J 8 7
              ◊ 9 4 2
              ♣ A K 10 6
```

```
♠ Q 9 8 6 3        N        ♠ K 2
♡ 5                         ♡ 4 3 2
◊ K 10 6 3      W     E      ◊ J 8 7 5
♣ 9 4 2            S         ♣ Q J 8 3
```

```
              ♠ A 10 7 4
              ♡ A Q 10 9 6
              ◊ A Q
              ♣ 7 5
```

Playing in six hearts, South has won the spade lead, eliminated the clubs, drawn two rounds of trumps, and exited with the 10 of spades, creating the impression that he began with A 10 alone. Did you fall into the trap of supposing that since a spade would apparently allow a ruff and discard (or sluff, ruff, if that is your idiom), you must risk a low diamond?

The problem illustrates the need to count, which is the beginning, the middle, and almost the end, of good defense. Partner's play of the spade deuce indicates an original even number of spades (current count). If partner had four spades, declarer has four black cards. Even if declarer has six hearts, he must have three diamonds. So a ruff/sluff can't help him.

You may reply that a diamond lead won't hurt the defense either since declarer's third diamond is a loser. What third diamond!? Declarer has executed a diabolical deception. Did he catch you napping? And this is only problem number one!

2. Confidence

Dealer South Both sides vulnerable

$$\spadesuit \text{ Q } 10\ 9\ 8\ 4$$
$$\heartsuit \text{ 3}$$
$$\diamond \text{ K } 9\ 4\ 2$$
$$\clubsuit \text{ } 7\ 6\ 3$$

$$\spadesuit \text{ A J 5}$$
$$\heartsuit \text{ A J}$$
$$\diamond \text{ J 10}$$
$$\clubsuit \text{ A Q } 10\ 8\ 4\ 2$$

South	West	North	East
1◇	2♣	2◇	Pass
3◇	Pass	Pass	3♡
Pass	Pass	3♠	Pass
4◇	Double	Pass	Pass
Pass			

Your partner has failed to turn up for the first session of a pair game, and the tournament director has provided you with a substitute. You have an early opportunity to establish mutual confidence.

Your lead of the jack of diamonds is covered by the king, 3 and 5. Declarer leads a low spade from dummy, partner plays the 2 and declarer the king. How will you defend?

Answer 2

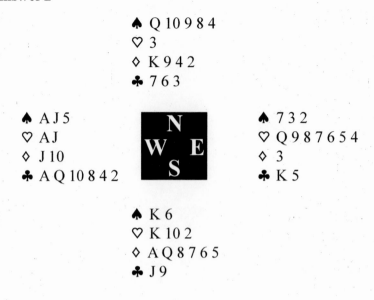

<pre>
                    ♠ Q 10 9 8 4
                    ♡ 3
                    ◊ K 9 4 2
                    ♣ 7 6 3

    ♠ A J 5   N   ♠ 7 3 2
    ♡ A J   W   E   ♡ Q 9 8 7 6 5 4
    ◊ J 10   S   ◊ 3
    ♣ A Q 10 8 4 2   ♣ K 5

                    ♠ K 6
                    ♡ K 10 2
                    ◊ A Q 8 7 6 5
                    ♣ J 9
</pre>

South plays in four diamonds doubled after West has overcalled in clubs and East in hearts. West's diamond lead is won in dummy and declarer leads a low spade, covered by the 2 and king.

Clearly you need to determine whether partner has the king of hearts or the king of clubs. If you win the first spade you will have to guess. However, partner has played the 2, suggesting an odd number, so it must be safe to duck. On the next spade partner will have an opportunity for a suit-preference signal-playing the 7 if he has the king of hearts, the 3 if he has the king of clubs. If you defend on that basis, partner's second spade will be the three, suggesting club strength. Now it is easy to cash the clubs and a heart without risking the daring heart underlead.

3. Telephone Wire

Dealer South   Both sides vulnerable

<pre>
                    ♠ 10
                    ♡ K Q 3
                    ◇ J 10 9 7
                    ♣ 10 9 7 4 2

        ♠ K 6 5 4 3
        ♡ A J 7
        ◇ A 6 3
        ♣ 8 3
</pre>

South	West	North	East
1♠	Pass	1NT	Pass
3♣	Pass	3NT	Pass
4♠	Pass	5♣	Pass
Pass	Pass		

It is rubber bridge, and for a moment you hoped you would be defending against a hated rival in four spades. Five clubs is less promising from your angle. You decide to lead the ace of diamonds, on which partner plays the 2 and declarer the king. What chance have you now to save the rubber? What do you lead at trick two?

Answer 3

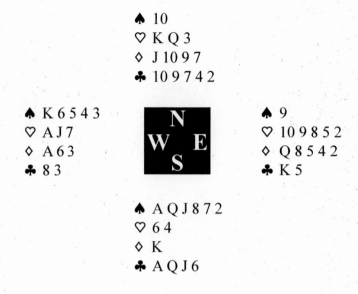

♠ 10
♡ K Q 3
◇ J 10 9 7
♣ 10 9 7 4 2

♠ K 6 5 4 3
♡ A J 7
◇ A 6 3
♣ 8 3

♠ 9
♡ 10 9 8 5 2
◇ Q 8 5 4 2
♣ K 5

♠ A Q J 8 7 2
♡ 6 4
◇ K
♣ A Q J 6

South plays in five clubs after an auction that has marked him with long spades. When the king of diamonds falls under the ace on the first trick, you place him with 6-2-1-4 or 6-1-1-5 distribution.

You expect to make your two aces, but where will the third trick come from? The best chance is that partner will hold K x of clubs. If that's the case, you can ensure a trick for the ♣K by leading the king of spades at trick two, attacking by overhead cable. South will win and lead a heart. You go up with the ace and lead another spade.

It would, of course, be a mistake to cash the ace of hearts at trick two, as this would allow South to enter dummy and pick up the trumps.

4. 'Down In Your Own Hand'

Dealer South Neither side vulnerable

                        ♠ Q J 8 6 3
                        ♡ A K J 6 3
                        ◊ 5 3
                        ♣ 5

    ♠ A 10 9 7
    ♡ 7 2
    ◊ A 6
    ♣ A 9 8 7 4

South	West	North	East
1♠	Pass	2♡	Pass
2NT	Pass	4♠	Pass
Pass	Pass		

North-South are playing the Blue Club, in which four-card majors are freely opened and 2NT is a weak rebid. You have prudently abstained from doubling four spades. You lead the ace of clubs, followed by the ace of diamonds, partner dropping a discouraging card in each case. What should you lead next?

Answer 4

　　　　　　　　　♠ Q J 8 6 3
　　　　　　　　　♡ A K J 6 3
　　　　　　　　　◊ 5 3
　　　　　　　　　♣ 5

♠ A 10 9 7　　　　　　　　　　　　♠ —
♡ 7 2　　　　　　　　　　♡ Q 10 9 8 4
◊ A 6　　　　　　　　　　　　　　◊ Q 9 8 4 2
♣ A 9 8 7 4　　　　　　　♣ 6 3 2

　　　　　　　　　♠ K 5 4 2
　　　　　　　　　♡ 5
　　　　　　　　　◊ K J 10 7
　　　　　　　　　♣ K Q J 10

This deal occurred in a match between Italy and Norway during the qualifying round of the 1970 Bermuda Bowl.

Defending against four spades, the Italian West successfully cashed his two side aces and with a sigh of content switched to a heart. A low spade to the king revealed the trump division, and with two entries to hand—a heart ruff and the king of diamonds—South was able to pick up West's trumps, losing only one trick.

West's partner might have spoken those bitter words, 'You had it down in your own hand.' To protect his trump holding, West must lead a diamond at trick three, removing one of South's entries before he knows about the 4-0 break in spades. South wins the diamond and leads the king of spades, the standard safety play. West wins and exits with a heart. South can come to hand with a heart ruff, but on the next lead of trumps West splits his 1097 and cannot be prevented from taking another trick.

5. How Right!

Dealer South N-S vulnerable

♠ A 10 5
♡ A K 5 3 2
◇ 8 4 2
♣ A 7

♠ K led

♠ 3
♡ 8 7 4
◇ K Q 10 7 5 3
♣ 8 6 4

South	West	North	East
1♣	2♠	3♡	Pass
4♣	Pass	5♣	Pass
Pass	Pass		

You are doing well in a pair event, playing with a partner who likes weak jump overcalls.

You'd like to get past your present opponents without a calamity, because they spoiled your score last time.

West leads the king of spades. Declarer ducks and partner follows with the queen of spades to dummy's ace. What is your plan?

Answer 5

```
              ♠ A 10 5
              ♡ A K 5 3 2
              ◇ 8 4 2
              ♣ A 7
```

```
♠ K Q J 9 4 2                        ♠ 3
♡ Q 10 9          N                  ♡ 8 7 4
◇ 9 6         W       E              ◇ K Q 10 7 5 3
♣ 3 2             S                  ♣ 8 6 4
```

```
              ♠ 8 7 6
              ♡ J 6
              ◇ A J
              ♣ K Q J 10 9 5
```

South plays in five clubs after West has made a weak jump overcall in spades. They won't be the only pair to bypass 3NT. West leads the king of spades. Declarer plays low from dummy and on the next trick covers the queen with the ace.

Has your partner misled the declarer by overcalling two spades on a 7-card suit? Did South perhaps forget the spade overcall? Anyway, you are going to get a good score at this table. You ruff and...

Too late! South has played you for a sucker, and how right he was! He wins the diamond return, plays three rounds of hearts, ruffing high, then leads the king of clubs and a club to the ace. Trumps are breaking now, and he obtains two discards on the long hearts.

If you think it out, the only reason declarer is letting you ruff away the ace of spades is because he hopes to use dummy's hearts. So instead of ruffing you must discard a diamond; not a heart, because this allows declarer to duck a diamond to you and later squeeze your partner in the majors.

6. Impersonation

Dealer South Neither side vulnerable

♠ K J 10 6 3
♡ A J 7
◊ J
♣ 10 8 5 3

♠ A Q 7
♡ 10 5 3 2
◊ 6
♣ A K 9 6 2

South	West	North	East
3NT	Pass	Pass	Pass

Imagine, if it is not too great a stretch, that you are on the French (or Austrian) women's team in the European Championship. The opening 3NT is described as "Gambling"—a solid minor suit with little outside strength. You lead the ace of clubs, on which partner drops the 4 and declarer the 7. How do you continue?

Answer 6

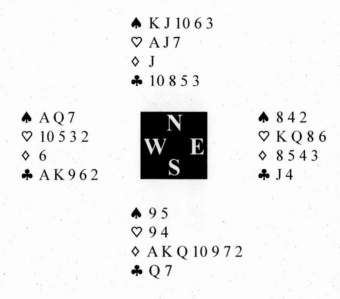

♠ K J 10 6 3
♡ A J 7
◊ J
♣ 10 8 5 3

♠ A Q 7
♡ 10 5 3 2
◊ 6
♣ A K 9 6 2

♠ 8 4 2
♡ K Q 8 6
◊ 8 5 4 3
♣ J 4

♠ 9 5
♡ 9 4
◊ A K Q 10 9 7 2
♣ Q 7

In the match between the French and Austrian ladies at Lausanne, South opened 3NT at both tables and West began with a high club.

The Austrian defender followed the ace of clubs with the king, establishing dummy's 10 of clubs as the ninth trick. The French West made a better try, leading a low club at trick two. This would have beaten the contract if partner had held ♣QJ4 or the queen of clubs and the K Q of hearts.

Since partner must be credited with the king of hearts, it cannot be wrong to lead a heart at trick two. And if declarer has the singleton 9 of hearts, or 9 x, the only way to defeat the contract may be to switch to the 10 of hearts.

7. Elusive

Dealer South E-W vulnerable

♠ J 5 3
♡ Q 9 4 2
◊ 8 3
♣ Q 10 9 5

♠ Q 10
♡ A K J 7 3
◊ K 9 2
♣ J 7 6

South	West	North	East
1♠	2♡	Pass	Pass
3◊	Pass	3♠	Pass
Pass	Pass		

You lead the king of hearts, on which partner plays the 10 and declarer the 6. It looks as though you will be able to make at least two hearts and the king of diamonds, but how will you arrive at two more tricks? How do you continue after the king of hearts?

Answer 7

```
                    ♠ J 5 3
                    ♡ Q 9 4 2
                    ◇ 8 3
                    ♣ Q 10 9 5

     ♠ Q 10              N              ♠ 9 6 4
     ♡ A K J 7 3      W     E           ♡ 10 5
     ◇ K 9 2             S              ◇ 7 6 4
     ♣ J 7 6                            ♣ A 8 4 3 2

                    ♠ A K 8 7 2
                    ♡ 8 6
                    ◇ A Q J 10 5
                    ♣ K
```

South plays in three spades after opening one spade and rebidding diamonds at the three level. On the lead of the king of hearts East plays the 10 and declarer the 6.

West must assume that South is 5-5 in spades and diamonds. If 6-5, he will always make the contract. And if he is 5-3-5-0, where will the fifth trick come from?

The best hope is to find partner with the ace of clubs and the 9 of spades. To beat the contract, you must, of course, cash the club trick before leading a third heart for a trump promotion, since otherwise declarer will play loser-on-loser. The winning defense is a club to the ace at trick two, heart back, and third heart, partner ruffiing with the spade 9, promoting a trick for the queen of spades.

Everyone has met this kind of situation many times, but somehow the right defense is seldom found.

8. In Tempo

Dealer South   N-S vulnerable

                    ♠ 10 7
                    ♡ K 9
                    ◊ K 7 6 3
                    ♣ Q 10 9 5 4

♠ K 9 8 5 4 2
♡ 10 6 3
◊ J 9 2
♣ K

South	West	North	East
1NT	Pass	2NT	Pass
3NT	Pass	Pass	Pass

South's 1NT is in the 15-17 range. Sitting West, you lead the 5 of spades. East wins with the ace and South plays the 6. East returns the 3 and South contributes the queen. How do you play at this point?

Answer 8

```
              ♠ 10 7
              ♡ K 9
              ◊ K 7 6 3
              ♣ Q 10 9 5 4

  ♠ K 9 8 5 4 2                    ♠ A 3
  ♡ 10 6 3          N              ♡ Q 8 7 5 2
  ◊ J 9 2        W     E           ◊ Q 8 4
  ♣ K              S               ♣ 7 6 3

              ♠ Q J 6
              ♡ A J 4
              ◊ A 10 5
              ♣ A J 8 2
```

South is in 3NT and you lead the 5 of spades. East wins and returns the spade three, South producing the queen on the second round.

This is not a testing problem, but it is important to play the right card 'in tempo'.

It is clear that South holds the jack of spades, since East, with AJ3, would certainly have returned the jack. West must decide whether to clear the spades, hoping to come in with the king of clubs, to win with the king of spades and look for tricks elsewhere, or to duck on this trick, with the risk of never making a trick with the king of spades.

The diagram shows why it would be fatal to win with the ♠K and clear the suit: this would induce declarer to drop the singleton king of clubs. To win with the king and look for tricks in one of the red suits is a vain hope. The best card to play on the second trick is the 4 of spades . This will make it look as if you have five spades and partner has A32. South should conclude that the spades are probably 5-3 and will take the best chance in clubs, finessing for the king.

9. Moment of Panic

Dealer North   Neither side vulnerable

　　　　　　　　♠ K 9 2
　　　　　　　　♡ —
　　　　　　　　◊ K J 9 8 5
　　　　　　　　♣ Q J 9 8 7

♠ A J 4 3
♡ K 10 8　　　
◊ 7 6
♣ A K 10 4

South	West	North	East
—	—	Pass	Pass
4♡	Double	Pass	Pass
Pass			

You were looking forward to a restful evening in the Mixed Pairs, but on the very first round you find yourself on the front line, and not playing too well.

You lead the king of clubs; partner plays the 2. As you may need two tricks in spades, you lay down the ace, but this is greeted by the 5 from partner and the 6 from declarer. Wondering now whether you may have to defend your double of the pre-emptive opening, you try the 7 of diamonds: jack, queen, ruff by declarer. It looks as though it was a mistake to lead the ace of spades; in any case the jack would have been better, giving you a chance to win two tricks when partner held 10 x x. After ruffing the diamond, South plays ace and jack of hearts. You win with the king, partner playing the 6 and 7. What hope remains?

Answer 9

```
              ♠ K 9 2
              ♡ —
              ◇ K J 9 8 5
              ♣ Q J 9 8 7

  ♠ A J 4 3        N          ♠ 10 5
  ♡ K 10 8                    ♡ 7 6
  ◇ 7 6        W     E        ◇ A Q 10 4 3 2
  ♣ A K 10 4      S           ♣ 6 5 2

              ♠ Q 8 7 6
              ♡ A Q J 9 5 4 3 2
              ◇ —
              ♣ 3
```

Defending against four hearts doubled, you lead the king of clubs and follow with the ace of spades. You switch to a diamond, which is ruffed. South plays the ace and jack of hearts.

In view of partner's 2 of clubs at trick one and his failure to echo in trumps, declarer must be either 2-8-0-3 or 4-8-0-1.

In the first case you will make a second trick in clubs eventually; at worst, you will have to apologize for not giving partner a ruff.

In the second case, however, you must return a spade. Otherwise, declarer will win the lead of a red suit and run his trumps, squeezing you in the black suits. But if partner has the 10 of spades, the spade return will break up the squeeze-even in the Mixed Pairs.

10. Next Bus

Dealer East   N-S vulnerable

$\quad\quad\quad\quad$ ♠ K J 5
$\quad\quad\quad\quad$ ♡ J 8 7 6 4
$\quad\quad\quad\quad$ ◊ 10 6 2
$\quad\quad\quad\quad$ ♣ A K

♠ 10 8 7 6 2
♡ A 2
◊ 4
♣ 10 9 6 5 3

South	West	North	East
—	—	—	1◊
1♡	Pass	4♡	Pass
Pass	Pass		

As West, you have a promising double of four hearts, but you don't altogether trust your partner's opening bids at this vulnerability.

You lead the 4 of diamonds, dummy plays low, and your partner's 9 is captured by the ace. South leads the 3 of spades to the king and ace. East exits with the queen of diamonds and South covers with the king. How do you plan the defense?

Answer 10

```
              ♠ K J 5
              ♡ J 8 7 6 4
              ◇ 10 6 2
              ♣ A K

  ♠ 10 8 7 6 2        N          ♠ A 9 4
  ♡ A 2                          ♡ K
  ◇ 4          W         E       ◇ Q J 9 7 5 3
  ♣ 10 9 6 5 3        S          ♣ Q 8 4

              ♠ Q 3
              ♡ Q 10 9 5 3
              ◇ A K 8
              ♣ J 7 2
```

South plays in four hearts after East has opened one diamond. Your lead of the 4 of diamonds is covered by the 9 and ace. Declarer leads a low spade to the king and ace. East exits with the queen of diamonds and South plays the king.

If you ruffed with the 2 of hearts and wondered what to play next, you missed the bus! It should be clear that South led a spade at trick two in the hope of establishing a quick discard. If he had held a low doubleton he would have finessed the jack, so he must have Q x.

Partner has a diamond winner, but how will you get him in to make it? Only by playing him for a singleton king of hearts! You must ruff with the ace of trumps and return the 2. Not too difficult when you see it in a book, but a neat coup to bring off at the table.

11. Mystery Trip

Dealer South   Neither side vulnerable

♠ 6 4
♡ K Q 5
◇ Q 7 6
♣ K J 8 3 2

◇ K led

♠ K Q 8 5
♡ J 3
◇ 4 3 2
♣ Q 9 7 6

South	West	North	East
2◇	3◇	3♡	Pass
4♣	Pass	6♣	Pass
Pass	Pass		

The two-diamond opening is 'Flannery', denoting four spades and five hearts, 12-15 points. How some American tournament players can think it clever to devote a useful opening bid to so specialized and by no means intractable a type is a mystery to the rest of the world.

West leads the king of diamonds and South, who is evidently 4-5-0-4, ruffs. At trick two he leads the 10 of clubs. West discards a diamond and dummy plays low. Well, you now know the entire hand, so how do you plan the defense?

Answer 11

```
              ♠ 6 4
              ♡ K Q 5
              ◊ Q 7 6
              ♣ K J 8 3 2

  ♠ 10 9 3          N          ♠ K Q 8 5
  ♡ 8 7 2      W         E     ♡ J 3
  ◊ A K J 10 9 8 5   S         ◊ 4 3 2
  ♣ —                          ♣ Q 9 7 6

              ♠ A J 7 2
              ♡ A 10 9 6 4
              ◊ —
              ♣ A 10 5 4
```

South, who has revealed his exact distribution in the bidding, plays in six clubs. He ruffs the diamond lead and runs the 10 of clubs.

It is clear that South has on top five hearts, the ace of spades, four top winners in clubs and, already, one ruff. That adds to eleven tricks, and if you take the queen of clubs he will have no difficulty in ruffing another diamond, using the king and queen of hearts for entries to dummy.

Although the play appears to surrender a tempo, you must retain control of the trump suit by ducking the 10 of clubs. The best that declarer can do is cross to the king of hearts, ruff a diamond, cash the ace of clubs, and return to dummy to play the king of clubs. But now you can ruff the third heart with the ♣Q and cash a diamond.

The idea of retaining a high card in the trump suit is familiar in other settings. An added feature here is that winning with the queen of clubs assists the declarer's communications.

12. Vantage Point

Dealer South   Neither side vulnerable

♠ 8 6 2
♡ Q 9 5
◇ A J 7 5 2
♣ K 8

♣ 10 led

♠ Q 10 3
♡ 7 4
◇ K Q 9 6
♣ A Q 5 2

South	West	North	East
1♡	Pass	2◇	Pass
4♡	Pass	Pass	Pass

West leads the 10 of clubs against four hearts, dummy plays the 8, and you win with the queen. You follow with the ace of clubs, on which South plays the jack and West the 9. What do you play now?

Answer 12

```
              ♠ 8 6 2
              ♡ Q 9 5
              ◊ A J 7 5 2
              ♣ K 8
```

```
♠ K J 7 5              N            ♠ Q 10 3
♡ 8                                 ♡ 7 4
◊ 8 4 3          W         E        ◊ K Q 9 6
♣ 10 9 7 6 3          S             ♣ A Q 5 2
```

```
              ♠ A 9 4
              ♡ A K J 10 6 3 2
              ◊ 10
              ♣ J 4
```

Your partner leads the 10 of clubs against four hearts. You win the first trick with the queen and follow with the ace, on which South plays the jack and West the 9.

Presumably South has a doubleton club and West's 9 is suit preference. Partner may think he wants you to play a spade, but with your strong holding in diamonds you know better. South's spade losers cannot run away so long as you prevent him from enjoying a long diamond.

If you return a spade at trick three South will take the ace, play the ace of diamonds and ruff a diamond, then use the three trump entries to win a trick with the fifth diamond. You must return a trump at trick three, removing one of the vital dummy entries before declarer can make good use of it. South will then be unable to escape from two spade losers.

13. Good but not Perfect

Dealer South   Both sides vulnerable

<pre>
                       ♠ A K Q 3
                       ♡ Q 4
                       ◊ J 7 3
                       ♣ K J 10 4

        ♠ 9 4
        ♡ A 6 5
        ◊ K 6 4 2
        ♣ A Q 5 3
</pre>

South	West	North	East
—	—	1♣*	Pass
1♡	Pass	1♠	Pass
2♡	Pass	3♡	Pass
4♡	Pass	Pass	Pass

* Unwilling to open 1NT with two unstopped suits

You lead the 2 of diamonds, which is covered by the 3, 9 and ace. South leads a heart to the queen and returns a heart to the jack. On these two tricks East plays high-low, indicating three trumps. How do you plan the defense?

Answer 13

♠ A K Q 3
♡ Q 4
◊ J 7 3
♣ K J 10 4

♠ 9 4
♡ A 6 5
◊ K 6 4 2
♣ A Q 5 3

♠ J 8 7 6
♡ 7 3 2
◊ Q 10 9 5
♣ 8 2

♠ 10 5 2
♡ K J 10 9 8
◊ A 8
♣ 9 7 6

This deal was the setting for a good play that was not quite good enough.

Defending against four hearts, West led the 2 of diamonds to the 9 and ace. Declarer played a heart to the queen and a heart back, East indicating three trumps by playing high-low.

From East's play of ◊9 on the first trick, West could place the declarer with at least one losing diamond, the 8, but a club ruff might be needed to defeat the contract. After some thought West took the second heart and led a low club. He expected dummy to win, and the play in clubs would indicate whether his partner held a doubleton.

Unfortunately for the defender, South ran the club to his 9 and drew the remaining trumps. West had the right idea but led the wrong club. West must lead the club queen to make sure that dummy wins the trick. Now declarer has no recourse.

14. Alternative Offer

Dealer South   Both sides vulnerable

```
                    ♠ 4
                    ♡ K Q J 8 4 2
                    ◊ Q 10 6 3
                    ♣ 7 2
```

```
    ♠ K 10 5
    ♡ 7 5 3
    ◊ K J 4
    ♣ J 8 5 3
```

South	West	North	East
1◊	Pass	1♡	Pass
2♣	Pass	3◊	Pass
6◊	Pass	Pass	Pass

No doubt North would have liked to rebid his hearts on the second round, but how many? Two hearts would not reflect the playing strength and three hearts would suggest a hand of better quality. Anyway, that is not your problem.

You are playing with a first-class partner in a team game. Your lead of the ♠5 runs to the queen and ace. Declarer plays ace and another diamond to your king. On the second diamond your partner discards the spade two, showing that he originally had an even number of spades. What do you play now?

Answer 14

<pre>
              ♠ 4
              ♡ K Q J 8 4 2
              ◊ Q 10 6 3
              ♣ 7 2
♠ K 10 5   ♠ Q 9 7 6 3 2
♡ 7 5 3   N   ♡ A 10 9 6
◊ K J 4   W   E   ◊ 7
♣ J 8 5 3   S   ♣ 9 4
              ♠ A J 8
              ♡ —
              ◊ A 9 8 5 2
              ♣ A K Q 10 6
</pre>

After a jump preference in diamonds, South has leapt to six diamonds. Your lead of a low spade runs to the queen and ace. South plays ace and another diamond, and partner's spade discard on the second round marks him with a six-card suit.

Since declarer has spade losers, his diamonds are ace-high, and he has spurned the 'Old Black', you can be sure that he is void of hearts. His clubs must be good, but you know they are not solid. He has three losers—two in spades and one in clubs—and can ruff only once in dummy, as he will need the ◊Q to draw your jack.

Suppose you exit passively with the jack of diamonds. Needing at least one trick from hearts, declarer will take a ruffing finesse. He will dispose of two spades on the hearts and ruff a club.

Are you getting warm? You know that the king of spades will give South a trick, establishing the jack, but it will also give him an option. He will ruff and lead the ♡K from the table. You can trust your partner to have drawn the right inferences from the bidding and to duck smoothly. Then South may ruff and rely on the clubs.

The point is that if you force declarer to play on hearts, he cannot go wrong. So you scheme to give him an alternative. Of course, against an equally clever declarer, all your scheming may come to naught. If you did have the heart ace, all you would have to do to beat the contract is exit with the diamond jack.

15. Unfamiliar Angle

Dealer South   Neither side vulnerable

♠ A 3
♡ 10 5 3
◇ K 9 8 6 3
♣ K J 7

♠ K Q 10 8 4
♡ A Q 8 6
◇ 5 2
♣ 5 3

South	West	North	East
1♣	1♠	2◇	3♠
4♣	Pass	5♣	Pass
Pass	Pass		

After years of honest endeavor you have earned the right to play in the Life Masters' Pairs. Quite soon you have a chance to demonstrate that you are not out of your league.

You lead the king of spades against five clubs. Dummy plays the 3, East the 2 (count) and declarer the 7. What do you play next?

Answer 15

```
              ♠ A 3
              ♡ 10 5 3
              ◇ K 9 8 6 3
              ♣ K J 7
♠ K Q 10 8 4         N          ♠ J 9 6 5 2
♡ A Q 8 6      W         E      ♡ K 7 4 2
◇ 5 2               S          ◇ Q J 7
♣ 5 3                          ♣ 2
              ♠ 7
              ♡ J 9
              ◇ A 10 4
              ♣ A Q 10 9 8 6 4
```

Defending against five clubs, you lead the king of spades, which holds the trick, East playing the 2 and declarer the 7.

Before seeing the full diagram, did you conclude that South held K x of hearts and was trying to keep East out of the lead? Did you therefore continue with a 'safe' spade?

This analysis does not stand up for a number of reasons. For one thing, East's 2 of spades suggests an odd number, probably five. (There are other possible interpretations, but your partnership style is to show distribution.) Secondly, if South has a doubleton spade and a loser in diamonds, the ace of hearts will suffice to beat the contract.

South has made a deceptive play that looks like a standard communication play, generally presented from the angle of the declarer. He plans to discard a diamond on the ace of spades and establish diamond winners without giving the defense a second chance. To justify your presence in a top-class event, you must lay down the ace of hearts at trick two. (Perhaps your partner could have helped by dropping the jack of spades on the first trick-but if you failed to switch, don't try to shift the blame!)

16. Early Embarrassment

Dealer East   Neither side vulnerable

<pre>
                        ♠ K 10 5
                        ♡ 8 4
                        ◊ J 6 5 3
                        ♣ A Q 8 4
    ♠ 8 6 4 2
    ♡ J 5 3
    ◊ K 7
    ♣ J 9 5 2
</pre>

South	West	North	East
—	—	—	Pass
1♠	Pass	2♣	Pass
2NT	Pass	3♠	Pass
4♠	Pass	Pass	Pass

South's 2NT was constructive, 15-17 in principle.

Cast your mind back to the time when you were a young player, aiming to make your reputation. Your opponents, in a Swiss team event, are world-weary experts. You make your mark at once by leading the king of diamonds from Kx. This passes off well, for partner turns up with A Q 9 4. On the third diamond you discard a heart. Partner follows with a fourth diamond, to kill dummy's jack. South ruffs with the ♠9. What is your plan from this point?

Answer 16

```
              ♠ K 10 5
              ♡ 8 4
              ◇ J 6 5 3
              ♣ A Q 8 4

  ♠ 8 6 4 2       N        ♠ 3
  ♡ J 5 3      W     E     ♡ K 10 9 6 2
  ◇ K 7           S        ◇ A Q 9 4
  ♣ J 9 5 2                ♣ 10 7 3

              ♠ A Q J 9 7
              ♡ A Q 7
              ◇ 10 8 2
              ♣ K 6
```

You have hit on the lead of ◇ K against four spades. You discard a heart on the third diamond and South ruffs the fourth round with ♠9.

Your side has made three tricks. If your partner holds the king of clubs he will surely take it. The interesting card is the king of hearts. If declarer holds ♡A Q, a finesse will give him the contract, but it is possible, is it not, that he will see the prospect of a squeeze should you hold the king of hearts with your four clubs.

Perhaps you thought of giving him a nudge in the wrong direction by discarding the jack of hearts? Good try, but there's a better play. What about underruffing, like a man seeking to postpone the evil day? When, later, you discard another heart, the declarer may well think that you have left yourself with a singleton king.

The defensive idea is quite easy to remember: when you know that you must guard one suit, pretend that you hold a critical card in another suit. Here, you underruff to further the illusion.

17. Implacable

Dealer South   E-W vulnerable

$\qquad$ ♠ 5 3
$\qquad$ ♡ K Q 7 6
$\qquad$ ◊ 7 6 5 4
$\qquad$ ♣ A Q 2

♠ Q 10 8 6 4
♡ 9 4 2
◊ A Q 10
♣ K 7

South	West	North	East
1♡*	1♠	3♡	Pass
4♡	Pass	Pass	Pass

* Four card majors, a la Acol

After a tiring session in the afternoon you would like to relax over dinner, but someone starts writing on the inevitable napkin. His hands usually have a point to them, so you give him your attention.

You lead the 6 of spades against four hearts and partner's jack is headed by the ace. South cashes the ♠ K, East's 2 indicating an original even number, then plays ace, king and queen of hearts. Partner follows with the ♡J 10, then discards the ♣J. At trick six a diamond is led to the 9, jack and queen. What, you are asked, do you do now?

Answer 17

	♠ 5 3	
	♡ K Q 7 6	
	◊ 7 6 5 4	
	♣ A Q 2	

♠ Q 10 8 6 4		♠ J 9 7 2
♡ 9 4 2	**N**	♡ J 10
◊ A Q 10	**W E**	◊ 9 8
♣ K 7	**S**	♣ J 10 9 8 6

♠ A K
♡ A 8 5 3
◊ K J 3 2
♣ 5 4 3

Playing in four hearts, South makes two spades, draws three trumps, East discarding the ♣J, then runs a diamond to the 9, jack and queen.

From the play it looks as though South is 2-4-4-3 or possibly 2-4-5-2. To exit with a club will be useless, for South will cash two clubs and exit with a diamond, leaving you on play. You can afford to give declarer two ruff-and-discards, so long as you can prevent him from enjoying a long diamond. So you lead a spade; he ruffs in dummy and plays a second diamond; you win and lead the fourth round of spades, taking his last trump. He takes the club finesse and leads a third diamond. But, like Horatio at the bridge, you win and cash the last spade for down one.

You give the napkin man the right answer eventually, but he is implacable. As you pick up your knife and fork he goes on: 'Could the declarer have made the contract at double dummy?'

This time, you let him tell you. South cashes the ♠A K, as before, takes only two trumps with the king and ace, finesses the ♣Q and leads a diamond. West can do no better than try the same defense, leading a spade. South takes the force, discarding a club from dummy, and leads another diamond. The difference is that if West now plays a fourth spade, South can ruff with his last trump. This way, he makes six tricks in the trump suit, two in spades and two in clubs; but none in diamonds!

18 . Another Tale of Hoffman

Dealer East   Neither side vulnerable

        ♠ K Q J 6 4 2
        ♡ Q 9 4
        ◇ 7 3 2
        ♣ 5

♠ 5
♡ A K J 8
◇ K Q J 6 4
♣ K 7 3

South	West	North	East
—	—	—	Pass
1♡	2◇	2♡	4◇*
4♡	Double	Pass	Pass
Pass			

* Preemptive! Really preemptive!!

Your best action over one heart is debatable. Some players would prefer a trap pass, others would double despite the singleton spade. You decide on two diamonds, hoping that something will develop. North, playing five-card majors, opted to raise to two hearts rather than respond two spades which he feared would show a stronger hand. You are thrilled to hear South bid four hearts.

You lead the king of diamonds. South wins and leads a heart. You play the king, East discarding the 2 of clubs, and lead a second diamond, which South ruffs. Declarer leads another heart. How do you plan your defense at this point?

Answer 18

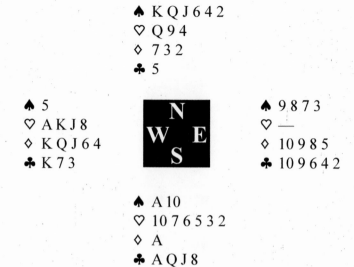

                    ♠ K Q J 6 4 2
                    ♡ Q 9 4
                    ◇ 7 3 2
                    ♣ 5

    ♠ 5   ♠ 9 8 7 3
    ♡ A K J 8   ♡ —
    ◇ K Q J 6 4   ◇ 10 9 8 5
    ♣ K 7 3   ♣ 10 9 6 4 2

                    ♠ A 10
                    ♡ 10 7 6 5 3 2
                    ◇ A
                    ♣ A Q J 8

In his book, Hoffman on Pairs Play, Martin Hoffman describes the play of this deal from the angle of the declarer. West led a diamond against four hearts doubled, won the next trick with the king of hearts, and led another diamond, South ruffing.

At this point Hoffman, who held the South cards, played on spades. This kills the defense. West can ruff the second spade, but there is still a trump entry to dummy.

When declarer errs and leads a second heart, you must duck, allowing dummy a heart entry which will prove premature. If declarer leads a third heart, you will win and play another diamond, forcing South to ruff with his penultimate trump. As South dare not play another trump, lest you win and cash your diamonds, he may play two rounds of spades. Using partner's count signal for guidance, you will ruff the second round and exit with a diamond, leaving South with two club losers.

If declarer plays on spades before conceding a third heart, you ruff the second spade, cash your high heart, and exit with a diamond. Declarer can play for down one after the second heart is won in dummy by ruffing out your club king.

19. Good Intention

Dealer North   Neither side vulnerable

♠ K J 5
♡ K 5 4
◇ A K J 10 7
♣ 8 4

♠ A 7 2
♡ Q J 10 3 2
◇ —
♣ 9 7 6 3 2

South	West	North	East
—	—	1◇	Pass
1♠	Pass	2♠	Pass
4♠	Pass	Pass	Pass

Sitting West, you lead the queen of hearts. Dummy plays low, East the 6 and declarer the 8. What do you do next?

Answer 19

```
                    ♠ K J 5
                    ♡ K 5 4
                    ◊ A K J 10 7
                    ♣ 8 4

    ♠ A 7 2                          ♠ 6 4
    ♡ Q J 10 3 2      N             ♡ A 7 6
    ◊ —            W     E          ◊ 8 6 4 3
    ♣ 9 7 6 3 2       S             ♣ Q J 10 5

                    ♠ Q 10 9 8 3
                    ♡ 9 8
                    ◊ Q 9 5 2
                    ♣ A K
```

South is in four spades. West leads the queen of hearts, dummy plays low, East the 6 and declarer the 8.

The play to the first trick suggests that declarer has at least two hearts, since with A 9 7 6 East would have dropped the 7 rather than the 6. If South has a second heart, a heart to the ace and a diamond back will defeat the contract.

The danger is that if West follows with the jack or 10 of hearts, East may not overtake. In a team game West followed with a well intentioned 3 of hearts, compelling partner to win. But, alas, East determinedly returned the queen of clubs, which, from his side, was not unreasonable.

There were two ways in which West might have averted this outcome. One was to lead something like the 7 of clubs at trick two. When later West comes in with the ace of spades and leads a low heart, partner can hardly go wrong.

The other possibility is to lead the ace of trumps before the low heart. So long as partner is half awake, he should realize that you have made a very unusual play, and for once, just might have an intelligent reason.

20. Off-stage

Dealer South   N-S vulnerable

```
              ♠ —
              ♡ A K 8 6 3 2
              ◊ 10 5
              ♣ A K Q 9 3
♠ Q 10 6 2
♡ J 7
◊ 4
♣ J 10 7 6 5 2
```

South	West	North	East
1◊	Pass	2♡	Pass
2♠	Pass	3♣	Pass
3♠	Pass	4♣	Pass
4♡	Pass	5◊	Pass
6◊	Pass	Pass	Pass

It's late at night, or early in the morning, and as your opponents wend their tortuous way to six diamonds you receive a general impression that South's distribution is similar to North's, but with spades and diamonds. You lead the ♡J, partner plays the 4 and declarer the queen. South ruffs a spade, partner playing the 5, and leads ◊10 from the table. East covers with the jack and declarer plays off ace, king and queen of diamonds, discarding a club and a heart from dummy.

Partner has followed to the diamond leads and it looks as though he began with ◊ J 9 8 7. Meanwhile, what do you discard on the second and third rounds of trumps?

Answer 20

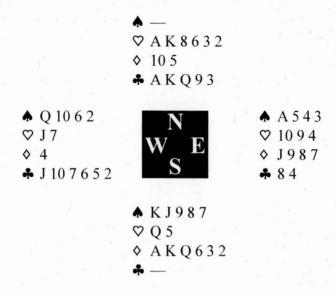

Playing in six diamonds, South wins the first trick with the queen of hearts, ruffs a spade, and leads ◇10, East covering with the jack. Declarer plays off the top diamonds, discarding a club and a heart from dummy.

This would be a testing hand at the table, because West might think he was off-stage, with nothing to do. But South is playing on, so there must be a chance. Partner is marked with a trump trick and must have the ace of spades (otherwise declarer has twelve tricks). If South is 5-2-6-0, he will be planning to lead his second heart to dummy and to discard spades on the top hearts and clubs.

Do you see the point? You must discard two spades on the diamonds—not a heart, which would disclose the heart position, and not clubs, which would suggest length in clubs. With no clue, South will surely rely on the clubs for his third discard, and East will ruff in time.

Difficult, but 'safe' discards are often very revealing.

21. The Saving Card

Dealer East   Both sides vulnerable

♠ 8 6 4 2
♡ K 9
◊ Q 9 4 2
♣ A 7 6

♡ 8 led   ♠ K Q 5
♡ A J 10 6 5 4 2
◊ —
♣ Q J 4

South	West	North	East
—	—	—	1♡
Double	Pass	1♠	2♡
4◊	Pass	5♣	Pass
6◊	Pass	Pass	Pass

Since North responded only one spade to the double, his five clubs must be a cue bid, suggesting a possible slam in diamonds.

West leads the 8 of hearts and dummy plays the 9. Your ace brings down the queen from declarer. What do you lead now?

Answer 21

```
              ♠ 8 6 4 2
              ♡ K 9
              ◊ Q 9 4 2
              ♣ A 7 6

  ♠ 10 9 7 3      N        ♠ K Q 5
  ♡ 8 7 3                  ♡ A J 10 6 5 4 2
  ◊ 8 5      W       E     ◊ —
  ♣ 8 5 3 2      S         ♣ Q J 4

              ♠ A J
              ♡ Q
              ◊ A K J 10 7 6 3
              ♣ K 10 9
```

South is in six diamonds, after you bid hearts twice, and the first trick goes to your ace of hearts.

It is not difficult to see that if you make the obvious return of the king of spades there will be a squeeze in the black suits. South, who is marked with long diamonds and all the outstanding strength, will play off all the trumps, enter dummy with the ace of clubs, and lead the king of hearts. You will be down to the ♠Q and the club Q J, and will be squeezed in front of South's ♠J and ♣K 10.

The deal illustrates one of the rarest and least known forms of defense to a squeeze-an early attack on the squeeze card. If you return a heart at trick two, South must make a premature discard. He will probably throw a club. Then you can retain your top spades in the end-game, and West's 8 of clubs will be the saving card.

22. Well Read

Dealer North   Both sides vulnerable

        ♠ J 4
        ♡ A 3
        ◊ K Q J
        ♣ A Q J 10 7 5

♠ A Q 8 3
♡ J 5 4
◊ 10 8 7 6
♣ 3 2

South	West	North	East
—	—	1♣	Pass
1♡	Pass	3♣	Pass
3NT	Pass	Pass	Pass

Guest of honor at a local club, you are pressed into playing a short match in partnership with the club's most promising young player. You lead the 6 of diamonds against 3NT, and when the dummy goes down it occurs to you that North's rebid of three clubs was not particularly venturesome. However, you must concentrate on defending 3NT. Your partner wins with the ace of diamonds and smoothly returns the 9 of spades, on which South plays low.

How do you defend? It would be terrible if, playing with the young genius, you were to make the first mistake.

Answer 22

```
              ♠ J 4
              ♡ A 3
              ◊ K Q J
              ♣ A Q J 10 7 5

  ♠ A Q 8 3                       ♠ K 9 6
  ♡ J 5 4         N               ♡ 10 9 8 2
  ◊ 10 8 7 6    W   E             ◊ A 9 3
  ♣ 3 2           S               ♣ 9 8 6

              ♠ 10 7 5 2
              ♡ K Q 7 6
              ◊ 5 4 2
              ♣ K 4
```

South is in 3NT, having shown some values by responding one heart to one club and bidding 3NT over the rebid of three clubs. You lead a diamond to the ace and partner returns the 9 of spades.

East has made a very good play. Did you diagnose it in time?

You could win with the queen of spades and lead a heart. This would produce five tricks if East held both the ♡K and the ♠K, but that would leave South very little for his 3NT bid.

You could let the 9 of spades run to the jack, but if East's spades are something like 9 7 x you will not be able to take more than two spades later.

No, you must give your young partner credit for having made the expert play of the 9 from K 9 x. When you win with the ♠Q and follow with the ♠3, the kibitzers will be able to applaud *both* defenders.

23. Not a Champion

Dealer West   Both sides vulnerable

♠ J 6
♡ 10
◇ A Q 8 7 6 4 3 2
♣ Q 6

♠ A 7 4
♡ A 9
◇ K 10 9
♣ A J 10 9 4

South	West	North	East
—	1♣	3◇	Pass
3NT	Double	Pass	Pass
Pass			

South is not a world champion, and as you can see four certain tricks in your own hand you risk a double of 3NT.

It could hardly help to lead a middle club, so you begin with the ace and follow with a low club. East plays the 5 and 3, South the 2 and 8.

Warned by your double, South leads a low diamond to the jack, East discarding a low heart. After winning with the king, what do you play next?

Answer 23

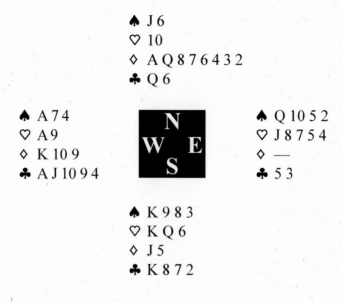

```
              ♠ J 6
              ♡ 10
              ◊ A Q 8 7 6 4 3 2
              ♣ Q 6

♠ A 7 4                        ♠ Q 10 5 2
♡ A 9                          ♡ J 8 7 5 4
◊ K 10 9                       ◊ —
♣ A J 10 9 4                   ♣ 5 3

              ♠ K 9 8 3
              ♡ K Q 6
              ◊ J 5
              ♣ K 8 7 2
```

South plays in 3NT doubled after West has opened one club and North has overcalled with three diamonds. West leads the ace of clubs and follows with a low club to dummy's queen. Warned by the double that the diamonds may be 3-0, South leads low to the jack and West is obliged to win.

At this point it is no use stabbing the air with your two aces, hoping for an encouraging signal. You must return a diamond, and the South hand will be destroyed long before he has finished running the suit. The play would be difficult for him even if he had stronger holdings in the major suits. This type of defense is often effective when dummy has a long suit and no side entry.

24. Justice

Dealer South   Neither side vulnerable

$\spadesuit$ A 10 6 5 3
$\heartsuit$ 5 4 3
$\diamondsuit$ 10 9 8 2
$\clubsuit$ A

$\spadesuit$ K J 4
$\heartsuit$ K 10 7 2
$\diamondsuit$ 4
$\clubsuit$ 10 9 7 5 3

South	West	North	East
1$\clubsuit$	Pass	1$\spadesuit$	Pass
3$\clubsuit$	Pass	3$\diamondsuit$	Pass
3NT	Pass	Pass	Pass

Justice has been done at last: you are playing for your country in a World Championship match. Sitting West, you lead the 2 of hearts to the jack and queen. South leads a club to the ace, on which East plays the 8, and follows with a spade to the queen, East playing the 2. How do you prove to the world that the selectors have made the right choice? Do you win this trick, or do you duck? If you win, what do you play next?

Answer 24

                    ♠ A 10 6 5 3
                    ♡ 5 4 3
                    ◊ 10 9 8 2
                    ♣ A

♠ K J 4   ♠ 9 8
♡ K 10 7 2   ♡ J 9 8
◊ 4   ◊ A K J 6 5 3
♣ 10 9 7 5 3   ♣ 8

                    ♠ Q 7
                    ♡ A Q 6
                    ◊ Q 7
                    ♣ K Q J 6 4 2

This hand is a good example of a line of thinking that is familiar to experienced players.

At both tables in a World Championship match South played in 3NT after showing strong clubs. (East might have doubled three diamonds, obviously, but he did not do so.) Your lead of the ♡2 ran to the jack and queen. Declarer crossed to the ace of clubs and led a spade to the queen.

It is no use ducking, because South will then make five clubs, two spades and two hearts. And it is no use winning with ♠K and leading a safe heart, for when South discovers that the clubs are not breaking he will be forced to a finesse of the ♠10.

What you must do-as Bob Hamman did at one table-is return a low spade before declarer knows that the clubs are not breaking. At this point he will surely refuse the finesse, expecting to take nine tricks. He will actually take seven!

25. Message Misunderstood

Dealer South   Neither side vulnerable

                    ♠ K 6 2
                    ♡ A 10
                    ◇ J 8 4
                    ♣ K J 8 5 2

    ♠ 9 5
    ♡ Q 8 6 5 4 3
    ◇ A Q 2
    ♣ A 9

South	West	North	East
South	*West*	*North*	*East*
3♠	Pass	4♠	Pass
Pass	Pass		

Having no very attractive lead, you begin with the ace of clubs. 'May not be enough for you,' remarks North as he puts down his dummy. Partner plays the 3 of clubs on the first trick and declarer the 10. Your general principle is 'No suit preference signals at trick one unless there can be be no other meaning,' so on the whole you take partner's 3 as count, signifying an odd number. What do you lead next?

Answer 25

<pre>
              ♠ K 6 2
              ♡ A 10
              ◊ J 8 4
              ♣ K J 8 5 2

  ♠ 9 5   ♠ J
  ♡ Q 8 6 5 4 3   N   ♡ K J 7
  ◊ A Q 2   W   E   ◊ K 9 6 3
  ♣ A 9   S   ♣ Q 7 6 4 3

              ♠ A Q 10 8 7 4 3
              ♡ 9 2
              ◊ 10 7 5
              ♣ 10
</pre>

This is not a complicated affair, but it illustrates a situation where misunderstanding can easily arise.

South opens three spades and is raised to four. You lead the ace of clubs: 3 from East, 10 from South.

You must certainly switch to a diamond. If you try a heart, for example, declarer will have enough entries to establish a tenth trick by means of a ruffing finesse against East's queen of clubs. Apart from which, South, who has opened three spades, is not very likely to hold the king of diamonds.

At the table West switched to the ace of diamonds, East encouraged, and West followed with the queen. There was now a small calamity: East officiously overtook with the king and tried to give his partner a diamond ruff.

'Why didn't you follow with a low diamond?' East demanded. 'I read you for A Q alone.'

To lead the ace of diamonds and follow with the 2 is also unsatisfactory. East may think that you have four diamonds and may try to give you a club ruff.

The best card to lead, when you attack a suit from A Q x(x) is the queen. If this holds, you follow with the ace from A Q x and fourth best from a longer suit. It then follows as East maintained that the ace followed by the queen signifies A Q alone.

26. Forcing Tactics

Dealer South   Both sides vulnerable

♠ A K 10 4
♡ J 8 6
◊ Q 7 5 3
♣ K 6

♡ 3 led

♠ J 7
♡ A 9 4
◊ J 4 2
♣ Q 10 7 3 2

South	West	North	East
1NT	Pass	2♣	Pass
2◊	Pass	3NT	Pass
Pass	Pass		

South's 1 NT opening is described on the card as 16-18. Whether it is sensible, with 13 points and honors in all suits, to use Stayman is doubtful, but this is not your concern. Partner leads the 3 of hearts, dummy plays low, and you must think about saving overtricks in a strong match point field. How do you begin?

Answer 26

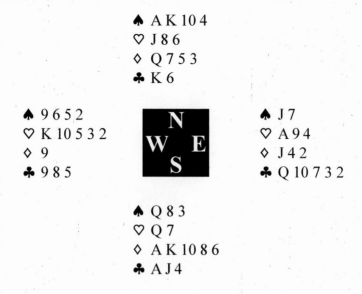

♠ A K 10 4
♡ J 8 6
◇ Q 7 5 3
♣ K 6

♠ 9 6 5 2
♡ K 10 5 3 2
◇ 9
♣ 9 8 5

♠ J 7
♡ A 9 4
◇ J 4 2
♣ Q 10 7 3 2

♠ Q 8 3
♡ Q 7
◇ A K 10 8 6
♣ A J 4

South, who has opened a 16-18 notrump, plays in 3NT. West leads the 3 of hearts and dummy plays low.

Partner, who has led his own suit from a very weak hand, probably has five hearts to the king or queen. At the table you would win with the ace and return the 9—admit it!

Now give the matter a little more thought. Since South's advertised minimum is 16 and you can see 21 in dummy and your own hand, partner's maximum is 3-either the king of hearts or the queen of hearts and the jack of clubs.

The danger of the orthodox defense is that partner may duck when you return the 9 of hearts at trick two and may not take a trick with the heart king until the next hand. Instead of saying at the end of the hand 'What was the point of holding up—you could see I had no entry', *force* West to do the right thing by winning with the ♡A and returning the 4. Reading you for a doubleton, he will see no reason to hold up the king.

This line of thinking (Don't give partner a chance to hold up a winner he may never make) is very important in match point play.

27. One of Those Things

Dealer South   E-W vulnerable

♠ 6 3
♡ 9 3
◊ A Q J 8 3
♣ K 8 6 3

♡ 5 led

♠ K J 10 9
♡ A K J 6 4
◊ 10 4
♣ J 5

South	West	North	East
1♠	Pass	2◊	Pass
2NT	Pass	3NT	Pass
Pass	Pass		

South's 2NT is described as 15-16. Your partner, who has been on top of his game, leads the 5 of hearts. How do you plan the defense?

Answer 27

```
              ♠ 6 3
              ♡ 9 3
              ◇ A Q J 8 3
              ♣ K 8 6 3

♠ 5 2                              ♠ K J 10 9
♡ Q 8 5         N                 ♡ A K J 6 4
◇ 9 7 6 5    W     E              ◇ 10 4
♣ 10 9 4 2      S                 ♣ J 5

              ♠ A Q 8 7 4
              ♡ 10 7 2
              ◇ K 2
              ♣ A Q 7
```

South plays in 3NT and West leads the 5 of hearts. In a world championship match two celebrated players had a celebrated misunderstanding. East played king and ace of hearts, West omitted to unblock, and after the queen of hearts South made the next nine tricks for his contract.

East had to play off the top hearts because declarer might have held a doubleton queen, and if East had held only four hearts it might have been fatal for West to drop the queen on the second round.

Was it, then, just 'one of those things'? As Jeff Rubens pointed out, when reporting the deal in the *Bridge World*, a simple convention will avert this kind of misfortune. The convention, just a commonsense understanding, really—is 'Unusual play calls for unusual play.' Knowing that he wants his partner to unblock from Qxx, East should begin with an ace and king of hearts, not the usual king and ace. There are many occasions where this kind of play will help; for example, when dummy holds x x x and East leads the suit from A K J 10.

28. Not as Planned

Dealer South   N-S vulnerable

♠ J 10 7 3
♡ K 8 5
◇ Q 6 2
♣ 10 7 4

♣ K led

♠ 6 5
♡ J 9
◇ A 10 8 7 4
♣ A Q 6 2

South	West	North	East
1♠	Pass	2♠	Pass
Pass	Pass		

Some players would respond 1 NT on the North hand, but surely it is better to raise with four card support.

Your partner leads a dynamic king of clubs and follows with the 8, which you win. Can you form a plan that may enable your side to beat two spades?

Answer 28

                    ♠ J 10 7 3
                    ♡ K 8 5
                    ◇ Q 6 2
                    ♣ 10 7 4

    ♠ A 8   ♠ 6 5
    ♡ Q 7 6 4 3 2   ♡ J 9
    ◇ 9 5 3   ◇ A 10 8 7 4
    ♣ K 8   ♣ A Q 6 2

                    ♠ K Q 9 4 2
                    ♡ A 10
                    ◇ K J
                    ♣ J 9 5 3

West leads the king of clubs against two spades and follows with the 8. Evidently West has K x and South J 9 x x.

A player who leads the king from K x against a part-score contract normally has—or ought to have—a control in the trump suit, either A x or K x x. Otherwise, the risk is not justified.

After the lead you can see three tricks in clubs and one in diamonds, and it is fair to assume, as just noted, that partner has a trick in spades.

You haven't much chance of finding West with the ace of hearts or the king of diamonds, but suppose he has three low diamonds? Just continue with the ace of clubs and a fourth round, enabling partner to discard two diamonds. This attractive and easy to miss defense sets up a sixth trick by way of a diamond ruff, instead of the club ruff that partner was expecting.

29. Prize-winner

Dealer South   Both sides vulnerable

```
              ♠ K
              ♡ K J 5
              ◊ J 10 8 7 5 2
              ♣ 6 4 2
♠ J 9 8 6 4 3      N
♡ Q 7 3         W     E
◊ A K              S
♣ Q 5
```

South	West	North	East
1♣	Pass	1◊	Pass
1♡	1♠	2◊	Pass
2NT	Pass	3NT	Pass
Pass	Pass		

In the system played by North-South, a rebid of 1 NT would indicate a minimum hand.

You have ploughed through Terence Reese's annual competition in the *Observer* and believe that you have correctly interpreted his bidding idiosyncrasies. It would be a pity to stumble on the play problem.

You lead the 6 of spades against 3NT. Partner plays the 2 and declarer the 5. On a diamond from dummy East plays the 3 and declarer the queen. What is your next move?

Answer 29

```
              ♠ K
              ♡ K J 5
              ◇ J 10 8 7 5 2
              ♣ 6 4 2

♠ J 9 8 6 4 3                    ♠ 10 7 2
♡ Q 7 3                          ♡ A 9 4
◇ A K                            ◇ 6 4 3
♣ Q 5                            ♣ J 10 8 3

              ♠ A Q 5
              ♡ 10 8 6 2
              ◇ Q 9
              ♣ A K 9 7
```

Defending against 3NT, you lead the 6 of spades to dummy's king. A diamond from dummy is covered by the 3, queen and king.

It is clear that South holds ♠ A Q x and it is going to be impossible to beat the contract unless you can shut out dummy's diamonds. You accomplish this by leading the queen of hearts, a little known blocking play. If the queen is covered by the king, East must duck, of course. To lead a low heart instead of the queen is not so effective. South will let this run to the 9 and 10 and will enter dummy later by finessing the jack.

30. Never Volunteer

Dealer North Both sides vulnerable

♠ Q J 10 9 3
♡ K 8 7
◇ J 7 5 3
♣ 2

◇ K led

♠ K 7 6 5 4
♡ A Q 6 5 2
◇ 10 2
♣ J

South	West	North	East
—	—	Pass	Pass
3♣	Pass	Pass	Double
Pass	Pass	Pass	

West begins with king, ace and another diamond. You ruff with your lone trump and South follows, having begun with Q 9 8. What do you play now?

Answer 30

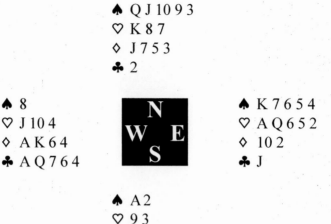

$\spadesuit$ Q J 10 9 3
$\heartsuit$ K 8 7
$\diamondsuit$ J 7 5 3
$\clubsuit$ 2

$\spadesuit$ 8
$\heartsuit$ J 10 4
$\diamondsuit$ A K 6 4
$\clubsuit$ A Q 7 6 4

$\spadesuit$ K 7 6 5 4
$\heartsuit$ A Q 6 5 2
$\diamondsuit$ 10 2
$\clubsuit$ J

$\spadesuit$ A 2
$\heartsuit$ 9 3
$\diamondsuit$ Q 9 8
$\clubsuit$ K 10 9 8 5 3

South, who has ventured an opening three clubs after two passes, plays in three clubs doubled. The defense begins with two top diamonds and a diamond ruff.

You don't want declarer to discard a losing heart on the fourth diamond. To prevent this, Peter Weichsel, in the Pairs Olympiad at New Orleans, made a sparkling play. He returned the king of spades, preventing South from gaining entry to dummy, however the spades were distributed.

Declarer won with the ace and led a second spade, which West ruffed. After two rounds of hearts the defense played a third spade, promoting an extra trump trick for the defense and obtaining a penalty of 1,400. The declarer, Jim Becker, who was acting as an emergency substitute, must have regretted his offer to volunteer.

31. Last Chance

Dealer East   Neither side vulnerable

```
                    ♠ Q 6 5
                    ♡ A K 7 6
                    ◊ J 4
                    ♣ A K 10 8
```

```
   ◊ K led                       ♠ A J 10 2
                                 ♡ 8 3 2
                                 ◊ 10 2
                                 ♣ Q 7 6 5
```

South	West	North	East
—	—	—	Pass
Pass	1◊	Double	1♠
Pass	Pass	Double	Pass
2♡	Pass	Pass	Pass

Your side goes quietly and South plays in two hearts. West begins with king, ace and 9 of diamonds, dummy pitching a spade as you ruff. Declarer follows with the six, seven, and queen.

Your expert partner has made no comment so far during the session, but there have been sundry indications that he has not been impressed by your bidding, play., or defense. Can you, on the final round, dazzle him with a display of clear thinking?

Answer 31

```
                    ♠ Q 6 5
                    ♡ A K 7 6
                    ◇ J 4
                    ♣ A K 10 8

    ♠ K 9 8              N              ♠ A J 10 2
    ♡ Q 10          W       E          ♡ 8 3 2
    ◇ A K 9 8 5         S              ◇ 10 2
    ♣ 4 3 2                            ♣ Q 7 6 5

                    ♠ 7 4 3
                    ♡ J 9 5 4
                    ◇ Q 8 7 6
                    ♣ J 9
```

South, responding to two take-out doubles by his partner, is playing in two hearts. West begins with king, ace and 9 of diamonds. Dummy discards a spade on the third round and East ruffs.

At this point there are two possible defenses to defeat the contract:(1) If South started with three diamonds and a likely 3-4-3-3 pattern, the contract will be defeated on sheer power. Your side will collect two more spades and a club.(2)   If South started with four diamonds (Q876) and a 3-4-4-2 pattern, no club trick is available, but the hand can still be beaten by trump promotion if partner has the Q10 doubleton of hearts. In this case, after cashing two spades, partner has to play a fourth diamond. Your heart eight will prevent a low ruff in dummy, and if declarer ruffs high, partner scores a trump trick.

In essence, partner must play a fourth diamond when declarer has four, and a black suit when declarer has three.

How can we make the decision foolproof for partner? Simply play the ace and deuce of spades! This shows your four card holding and marks declarer with three. Partner already knows how many diamonds declarer has. With a complete count on declarer's hand, partner will have no trouble making the right play.

Be sure to be appropriately modest in accepting partner's thanks for your thoughtful play.

32. Shaping Up

Dealer South   Both sides vulnerable

<pre>
                    ♠ A K 9 7
                    ♡ A 7 5
                    ◊ 3 2
                    ♣ A Q 10 6
</pre>

<pre>
   ♠ Q led   ♠ 4
                                              ♡ J 6
                                              ◊ A 10 8 7 6 5
                                              ♣ J 9 4 3
</pre>

South	West	North	East
South	*West*	*North*	*East*
3♠	Pass	6♠	Pass
Pass	Pass		

When partner leads a trump and the dummy goes down, it occurs to you that North's immediate raise has not helped your partner to find a diamond lead. However, South, a local professional, wins in dummy and leads a diamond himself.

You have had a moment or two to think about this and you decide fairly quickly not to go up with the ace. With ◊ Q J 9 4 West might have led a diamond instead of the trump queen; also, if South had held a singleton king he might have looked for a way to dispose of it on the clubs.

South wins with the ◊ K and exits with the 9 to West's queen. You have done the right thing so far, to the extent that you didn't solve declarer's KJ problem. Can you keep it up?

Answer 32

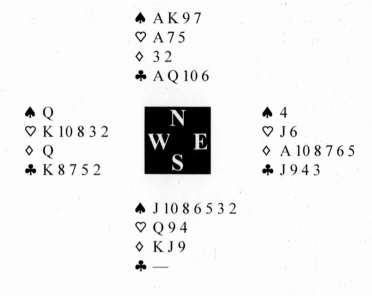

♠ A K 9 7
♡ A 7 5
◇ 3 2
♣ A Q 10 6

♠ Q
♡ K 10 8 3 2
◇ Q
♣ K 8 7 5 2

♠ 4
♡ J 6
◇ A 10 8 7 6 5
♣ J 9 4 3

♠ J 10 8 6 5 3 2
♡ Q 9 4
◇ K J 9
♣ —

South has opened three spades and has been raised to six. West leads the ♠ Q, won in dummy. A low diamond is won by the king and a diamond is returned, on which West plays the queen.

South, who is playing for money, must be credited with seven spades to the J 10. He is going to make the king of diamonds and a diamond ruff, plus two visible aces. That is eleven tricks, so the first conclusion is that, for the defense to have a chance, declarer must be void of clubs. The second conclusion is that South must hold the queen of hearts, as West would have led a heart from K Q.

Now things are beginning to shape up. If you let partner hold the queen of diamonds, South, after trying to bring down the king of clubs in three rounds, will reduce West to ♡ K x and ♣K in front of dummy's ♡A 7 and ♣Q, with a trump to come. To defeat the impending squeeze, you must overtake the ◇ Q with the ace and lead a heart.

33. In the Money

Dealer West   N-S vulnerable

♠ K Q 9 7
♡ A K Q 10 7
◇ 10 8
♣ 8 2

♠ A J 5
♡ 4 3
◇ 5 4 3
♣ A K J 7 5

South	West	North	East
—	1♣	Double	Pass
2◇	Pass	2♡	Pass
2♠	Pass	3♠	Pass
4♠	Pass	Pass	Pass

You are playing in a big-money event—the Cavendish Invitation Pairs. On your lead of the king of clubs East plays the 4 and declarer the 9. As the 3 is missing, you continue with the ace of clubs. Now East plays the 6 and declarer the 10. What do you make of this, and how do you see the defense?

Answer 33

```
                    ♠ K Q 9 7
                    ♡ A K Q 10 7
                    ◊ 10 8
                    ♣ 8 2

  ♠ A J 5              N              ♠ 10 3
  ♡ 4 3          W          E        ♡ 9 6 5 2
  ◊ 5 4 3             S              ◊ 9 7 6 2
  ♣ A K J 7 5                        ♣ 6 4 3

                    ♠ 8 6 4 2
                    ♡ J 8
                    ◊ A K Q J
                    ♣ Q 10 9
```

Defending against four spades, you begin with two top clubs, on which East plays the 4 and 6, South the 9 and 10. It looks as though East is concealing the 3 because he does not want to suggest a shift. So you continue with a third club, which is ruffed in dummy.

South comes to hand with a diamond and leads a low spade. You defeat the contract now by going up with the ace and leading a fourth club, promoting a further trump trick for the defense.

According to Eric Kokish, reporting in the *ACBL Bulletin*, Peter Nagy and Alan Sontag, at different tables, both found this defense from the West side. The moral is: when there's nothing else to play for, consider the possibility of a trump promotion.

Yes, we know that the bidding is bizarre. But, we merely report.

34. Excess Baggage

Dealer South   Neither side vulnerable

<pre>
                     ♠ 8 7 4 3
                     ♡ 6 5 4
                     ◊ K 8 4 2
                     ♣ K 10

    ♠ Q J 9
    ♡ A Q J   N
    ◊ J 10 9 7   W   E
    ♣ A Q 3   S
</pre>

South	West	North	East
1♠	1NT	2♠	Pass
4♠	Pass	Pass	Pass

You have a promising double of four spades, but your partner, at rubber bridge, has been unable to avoid a small trance over two spades. If you double now the opponents may claim a foul.

You lead the jack of diamonds, on which East plays the 5 and declarer the ace. South plays off ace, king and another spade, East discarding two low hearts and the 5 of clubs. What do you play when in with the queen of spades?

Answer 34

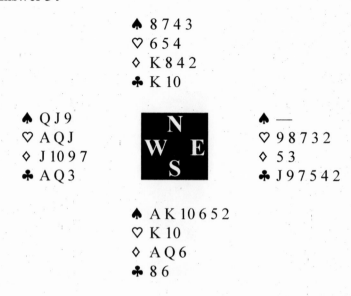

$\spadesuit$ 8 7 4 3
$\heartsuit$ 6 5 4
$\diamondsuit$ K 8 4 2
$\clubsuit$ K 10

$\spadesuit$ Q J 9
$\heartsuit$ A Q J
$\diamondsuit$ J 10 9 7
$\clubsuit$ A Q 3

$\spadesuit$ —
$\heartsuit$ 9 8 7 3 2
$\diamondsuit$ 5 3
$\clubsuit$ J 9 7 5 4 2

$\spadesuit$ A K 10 6 5 2
$\heartsuit$ K 10
$\diamondsuit$ A Q 6
$\clubsuit$ 8 6

South plays in four spades after West has overcalled with 1 NT. The lead of the diamond jack runs to the ace, partner dropping the 5. Declarer plays off three rounds of trumps, East discarding two low hearts and the 5 of clubs.

To exit with a diamond will expose you to a finesse, a heart will give a trick to the king, so it has to be a club—but which? If you play ace and another you will find it impossible to discard on three more rounds of trumps. A low club is no better: you will be able to discard a heart and two clubs on the spades, but will then be thrown in on the fourth round of diamonds.

To shift the burden imposed by your controls in three suits, you must exit with the queen of clubs. On the next two trumps you can throw the jack of hearts and the ace of clubs. If South plays his last trump you can afford to discard another heart because you still hold the precious 3 of clubs.

This type of play—the lead of the queen of clubs—is generally the answer when you hold 'too many' high cards for your own good in defense.

35. Many a Slip

Dealer North   E-W vulnerable

$$
\begin{array}{c}
\spadesuit \text{ A } 10\ 9\ 4 \\
\heartsuit \text{ J } 9 \\
\diamondsuit \text{ 7 } 5 \\
\clubsuit \text{ A Q J } 10\ 3
\end{array}
$$

♠ K J
♡ Q 8 4 2
◊ K Q 4 2
♣ 6 4 2

South	West	North	East
—	—	1♣	Pass
1♠	Pass	2♠	Pass
3♠	Pass	4♠	Pass
Pass	Pass		

On your lead of the king of diamonds partner plays the 9 and declarer the 3. Since you lead king from A K as well as from K Q, you conclude that partner has the ace of diamonds—he would not signal so emphatically from J 9 x x.

Defensive prospects seem quite good, but there's many a slip, as they say, 'twixt cup and lip.' This is the last hand of the Blue Ribbon Pairs. You are in contention. Can you finish strongly? What do you lead at trick two, and why?

Answer 35

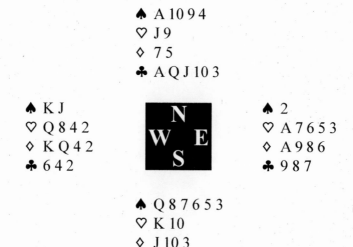

    ♠ A 10 9 4
    ♡ J 9
    ◇ 7 5
    ♣ A Q J 10 3

♠ K J   ♠ 2
♡ Q 8 4 2   ♡ A 7 6 5 3
◇ K Q 4 2   ◇ A 9 8 6
♣ 6 4 2   ♣ 9 8 7

    ♠ Q 8 7 6 5 3
    ♡ K 10
    ◇ J 10 3
    ♣ K 5

Defending against four spades. West holds the first trick with the king of diamonds, East signaling with the 9.

At the table this contract slipped away from the defenders in a most annoying fashion. West followed with the 2 of diamonds to his partner's ace, and East now conceived the notion of underleading the ace of hearts. South guessed right, cashed the ace of spades, and discarded his second heart on a club.

Who was at fault? West rather than East! West *knows* he has a trump trick, East doesn't. It cannot be wrong to cash the queen of diamonds and switch to a low heart, forcing East to play the ace if he has it. (Note that a heart at trick two might be a mistake: South might hold ♡ A K 10, instead of the king of clubs, and dispose of a diamond from dummy on the third round of hearts.)

This is quite a common situation. When you hold a winner that partner does not know about, aim to prevent him from making an imaginative underlead or other dangerous play.

36. Paradox

Dealer South   Neither side vulnerable

♠ 7 6 4
♡ 8 6
♦ Q 8 5
♣ K Q 10 8 4

♠ 10 led ♠ A 3
♡ Q 3
♦ J 9 7 4 2
♣ A 7 6 5

South	West	North	East
2♡	Pass	2NT	Pass
3♡	Pass	4♡	Pass
Pass	Pass		

South's two hearts is an Acol two bid, forcing for one round.

West leads the 10 of spades. You win with the ace, on which South plays the jack, and return a spade, won by the king, West playing low. South leads the jack of clubs, West plays the 2 and dummy the queen. Reading South for a singleton, you win with the ace. What do you play now?

Answer 36

              ♠ 7 6 4
              ♡ 8 6
              ◊ Q 8 5
              ♣ K Q 10 8 4

♠ 10 9 8 5 2   ♠ A 3
♡ K 5 2   ♡ Q 3
◊ 10 6   ◊ J 9 7 4 2
♣ 9 3 2   ♣ A 7 6 5

              ♠ K Q J
              ♡ A J 10 9 7 4
              ◊ A K 3
              ♣ J

West leads the 10 of spades against four hearts. South wins the second trick with the king and leads a club, won by the ace.

You have hopes of a spade ruff, but can hardly expect partner to hold the ace of diamonds as South has shown a powerful hand. Also, partner, if he held a diamond entry, would have played a higher spade at trick two. And, South did not cash the ace of hearts, as he probably would have if his hearts had been headed by the AKJ.

The most likely construction is that South holds the top diamonds and that his hearts are headed by A J 10. Oddly enough, the way to obtain a ruff is to lead a trump! If South plays the ace he will lose two heart tricks, and if he finesses the jack he will be open to a ruff in spades.

Needless to say, if East leads a diamond at trick four, South will win in dummy, discard a spade on the king of clubs, and lose only one trick in trumps.

37. Test of Nerves

Dealer South   Both sides vulnerable

♠ 10 8 7 6
♡ A J 10
◊ K 7
♣ 9 8 5 4

♠ A K J 5 3
♡ 6 5 2
◊ A 5
♣ Q 10 9

South opens with a Roman one club, usually a balanced 12-16 HCP. Your tactical scheme with a fairly good hand is to pass on the first round and enter later if the bidding suggests that your side has the balance of the cards. So you pass, and the bidding then develops in a somewhat nerve-racking way:

South	West	North	East
1♣	Pass	1◊	Pass
1NT	Double	Redouble	Pass
Pass	Pass		

Having steeled yourself to defend against 1 NT redoubled, you lay down the ace of spades, on which partner plays the 2 and declarer the 4. What next? You are playing in the first round-robin session of the World Championship, so you don't want to do anything foolish.

Answer 37

♠ 10 8 7 6
♥ A J 10
♦ K 7
♣ 9 8 5 4

♠ A K J 5 3
♥ 6 5 2
♦ A 5
♣ Q 10 9

♠ Q 2
♥ Q 8 7 3
♦ J 10 9 4 2
♣ J 2

♠ 9 4
♥ K 9 4
♦ Q 8 6 3
♣ A K 7 3

Defending against 1 NT redoubled, after South has opened the bidding, you lead the ace of spades. Partner cannot have more than 5 or 6 points, so it would be foolish to hope to beat the contract without developing the spades. If declarer has the queen of spades he will always have a spade guard, so it must be right to lead a low spade at trick two.

Kantar (West) and Eisenberg played this defense in a match between North America and South America. They must have been relieved to beat the contract, * for even after a spade to the queen and a club back, South can make seven tricks if he does everything right—playing West for a doubleton ace of diamonds and East for the queen of hearts. But this is a dangerous line, risking two down, and in practice the declarer made reasonably sure of six tricks by developing a long club.

* *You can say that again.* — E.B.K.

38. Boxed

Dealer North Both sides vulnerable

♠ Q J 10 2
♡ 10 2
◊ A J 9 8 7
♣ K 4

♠ 9 7 6 4
♡ K 9
◊ Q 5 4
♣ Q 9 7 5

South	West	North	East
—	—	Pass	Pass
1♣	Pass	1◊	Pass
1♠	Pass	4♠	Pass
4NT	Pass	5◊	Pass
6♠	Pass	Pass	Pass

You have often read accounts of world championship encounters and thought to yourself, 'I could have done better than that.' Now you have your chance.

You lead a trump. Declarer cashes the queen and jack, East discarding the ♡6, then runs the ◊7 , partner contributing the three. You to play.

Answer 38

```
              ♠ Q J 10 2
              ♡ 10 2
              ◇ A J 9 8 7
              ♣ K 4

  ♠ 9 7 6 4       N          ♠ 5
  ♡ K 9        W     E       ♡ Q J 8 6 5 3
  ◇ Q 5 4         S          ◇ 3 2
  ♣ Q 9 7 5                  ♣ J 8 6 2

              ♠ A K 8 3
              ♡ A 7 4
              ◇ K 10 6
              ♣ A 10 3
```

In the 1973 World Championship six spades was reached at both tables in a match between two American teams. Both Wests led a trump and one declarer made the best start, cashing ♠ Q J and then running the 7 of diamonds. This appears to win against any defense. Suppose West wins and attacks hearts. Declarer can take a club ruff, draw trumps, and make twelve tricks easily.

The diamond play marks declarer with ◇K 10 x, so let us try the effect of refusing to win the first diamond. When South repeats the finesse, you win and exit with a trump. Not quite good enough; declarer can still ruff a club, return to the ♡A, and later overtake the ◇ K.

Overtake the ◇K? Ah, now we're getting somewhere. Hold off the ◇7, win the next diamond, and lead a third diamond. South still needs a club ruff for his twelfth trick, but he is boxed for entries.

This would have been great play, of course, especially as the diamond queen must be held up without reflection. There are undoubtedly many opportunities for brilliancies of this sort. With Q x or Q x x over dummy's K J 10 it can hardly lose to hold up the queen and tempt declarer into a second finesse. There are many positions, too, where it must be good play to hold up a jack—when you hold AJx over K109, for example, declarer holding Qxxx.

39. Unwanted

Dealer West Neither side vulnerable

♠ K J 7
♡ K J 9
◇ 10 6 3 2
♣ Q 5 3

♠ 10 6 4
♡ A 7 6 5 4 3
◇ K 5
♣ 10 2

♣ K led

South	West	North	East
—	1♣	Pass	1♡
1♠	2♡	2♠	3♡
3♠	Pass	Pass	Pass

You are playing in a pairs event and at some risk you have driven your opponents to the three level. It is the sort of deal on which + 50 will be close to a top, —140 close to a bottom.

West begins with the king, ace and 8 of clubs. You ruff the third round, South following with the 4, 6 and 7. You can see four likely tricks for the defense. How will you play for a fifth?

Answer 39

                    ♠ K J 7
                    ♡ K J 9
                    ◇ 10 6 3 2
                    ♣ Q 5 3

    ♠ Q 5   ♠ 10 6 4
    ♡ Q 8 2   ♡ A 7 6 5 4 3
    ◇ J 9 4   ◇ K 5
    ♣ A K J 9 8   ♣ 10 2

                    ♠ A 9 8 3 2
                    ♡ 10
                    ◇ A Q 8 7
                    ♣ 7 6 4

South played in three spades after a part-score battle. The defense began with three rounds of clubs, East ruffing, and East saw no harm in exiting with a trump. After drawing trumps the declarer finessed the queen of diamonds, cashed the ace, and finessed the jack of hearts. If East wins this trick he can only return a heart, giving South two discards, and if he ducks, then declarer will simply give up a diamond.

It is easy to miss at the table, but East should realize that his ace of hearts is a dangerous card to keep. To cash the ace at trick four can hardly cost, for if declarer holds six spades and the A Q x of diamonds he can always establish a discard by finessing the ♡J.

40. To Ruff or Not to Ruff

Dealer South   E-W vulnerable

```
              ♠ 9 5 4
              ♡ K 7
              ◇ A K Q 4 2
              ♣ 9 7 4
                                    ♠ A K Q
   ♣ K led      N                   ♡ Q 10 6 4 2
              W   E                 ◇ 5 3
                S                   ♣ 8 6 2
```

South	West	North	East
1♠	Pass	2◇	Pass
2♡	Pass	3♠	Pass
4♠	Pass	Pass	Pass

    You are sitting at home, watching a Los Angles Lakers game on
television. * When the telephone rings you make the mistake of picking it
up. No hello; no name; no nothing—just this problem.
    The opening lead is the king of clubs. Declarer wins and cashes the
◇ A K, discarding the ♣10. Next comes the queen of diamonds from
dummy. Can you avoid your second mistake of the evening?

---

*Scarcely; Match of the Day, perhaps. — T .R.

Answer 40

<pre>
                    ♠ 9 5 4
                    ♡ K 7
                    ◊ A K Q 4 2
                    ♣ 9 7 4

  ♠ 7 6   ♠ A K Q
  ♡ 5 3   N   ♡ Q 10 6 4 2
  ◊ J 9 8 7 6 W   E   ◊ 5 3
  ♣ K Q 5 3   S   ♣ 8 6 2

                    ♠ J 10 8 3 2
                    ♡ A J 9 8
                    ◊ 10
                    ♣ A J 10
</pre>

South, who has bid spades and hearts, plays in four spades. He wins the club lead, discards ♣10 on the second round of diamonds, and follows with a third high diamond.

It is easy to gauge South's distribution. Presumably he is hoping to discard another club, so he must be 5-4-1-3. What will happen if you ruff and draw two trumps, to prevent heart ruffs? With only one trump left in dummy and ♡ A J 9 8 in hand, South will be forced to try the heart finesse and will make the contract.

Is there any chance if you refrain from ruffing? Yes, if West's trumps are good enough to prevent the declarer from ruffing twice in dummy. Left to his own devices, South is likely to play king, ace and a third heart, hoping that either the queen will come down in three rounds or that he will be able to ruff the third round low and the fourth with the ♠9. As the cards lie, West is able to insert the ♠6 on the third heart, and from that point the contract must fail.

In short, if you ruff the third diamond you force declarer into a winning line of play; if you discard a club, you have good chances.

41. His Idea

Dealer West   Neither side vulnerable

```
              ♠ K 2
              ♡ A 7 4 2
              ◊ 8 3
              ♣ A Q J 9 8
```

```
                                    ♠ 5 4
  ♣ 2 led                           ♡ K 10 9 6
                                    ◊ A 6 2
                                    ♣ 10 7 6 3
```

South	West	North	East
—	2◊	3♣	3◊
3♠	Pass	4♠	Pass
Pass	Pass		

It was not your idea to play a weak two diamonds, but partner proclaimed this as his method and it wasn't worth arguing. Now he leads what is presumably a singleton club against four spades, and the ace is played from dummy. It may not seem to matter which club you play, but . . . well, think about it.

Answer 41

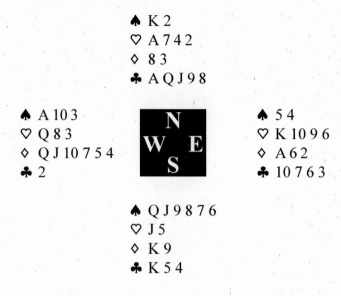

```
              ♠ K 2
              ♡ A 7 4 2
              ◇ 8 3
              ♣ A Q J 9 8

♠ A 10 3                          ♠ 5 4
♡ Q 8 3                           ♡ K 10 9 6
◇ Q J 10 7 5 4                    ◇ A 6 2
♣ 2                               ♣ 10 7 6 3

              ♠ Q J 9 8 7 6
              ♡ J 5
              ◇ K 9
              ♣ K 5 4
```

South plays in four spades after West has opened a weak two diamonds and East has supported the suit. West leads his singleton club and the ace is played from dummy.

Sitting East, it is more important to signal your entry than your length in clubs. For the defense to have any chance, West must hold a quick entry in trumps. If his spades are A x x and he wins the second round, then a heart shift cannot lose and may gain. Declarer will be unable to return to his hand without losing one spade, one heart, one diamond and a club ruff. You must play the 10 of clubs at trick one to attract a heart lead after the ace of spades.

42. Unhappy Memory

Dealer East   Neither side vulnerable

$\qquad\qquad\qquad$ ♠ A K 4
$\qquad\qquad\qquad$ ♡ A 6 5 2
$\qquad\qquad\qquad$ ◊ Q 7 6 5
$\qquad\qquad\qquad$ ♣ 8 2

♠ J 10 9 8 7 2
♡ J 4 3
◊ 8 2 $\qquad$
♣ K 7

At the time of this deal East-West were playing the 'mini-club' convention. East's opening one club denoted either 6 to 8 balanced or a genuine Precision one club.

South	West	North	East
—	—	—	1♣
2♣	Pass	2♡	Pass
3◊	Pass	4◊	Pass
5♣	Pass	6♣	Pass
Pass	Pass		

The North-South bidding was natural and East, obviously, had opened a mini-club.*

West led the jack of spades. Declarer played the king from dummy and the queen from hand. On the lead of the 2 of clubs East played the 4 and South the queen. As West, how would you plan the defense?

---

* *Do NOT try this at home!*

Answer 42

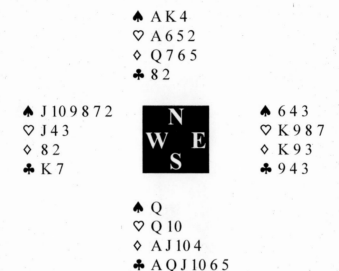

```
              ♠ A K 4
              ♡ A 6 5 2
              ◊ Q 7 6 5
              ♣ 8 2

♠ J 10 9 8 7 2                    ♠ 6 4 3
♡ J 4 3                           ♡ K 9 8 7
◊ 8 2                             ◊ K 9 3
♣ K 7                             ♣ 9 4 3

              ♠ Q
              ♡ Q 10
              ◊ A J 10 4
              ♣ A Q J 10 6 5
```

South played in six clubs after East had opened a mini-club, indicating 6 to 8 balanced. South won the spade opening in dummy and finessed the queen of clubs. How should West defend?

Did you have to think? Then it's too late. If you win the trick, South will use dummy's entry to lead ◊Q. And of course you are equally lost if you hesitate for a moment and then duck.

Terence Reese describes this deal, from the Tournament of Champions at Deauville, as one of his less happy memories. He won with the king, failing to display what the commentator called *'courage extraordinaire'*. It is usually right to decline a finesse that declarer is likely to repeat, and the idea did present itself, but not quickly enough. West was perhaps unlucky that the declarer was Chemla, who played the first two tricks in less time than it took you to read the description of them. It is not certain that he would have used dummy's entry to repeat the club finesse, but undoubtedly the best chance for the defense was to hold off.

43. Odd Information

Dealer South   Both sides vulnerable

♠ A
♡ K 8 6 4 3
◇ J 4 2
♣ K Q 10 5

◇ 9 led
♠ 7 4 2
♡ A 10
◇ K Q 10 3
♣ 8 7 3 2

South	West	North	East
1♠	Pass	2♡	Pass
3♣	Pass	4♣	Pass
4♡	Pass	4♠	Pass
5◇	Pass	6♣	Pass
Pass	Pass		

Asked whether four hearts in this sequence is a cue bid or expresses willingness to play in hearts, North states that in principle a bid at game level in a major is natural in their system.

West's lead of the 9 of diamonds is covered by the jack, queen and ace. South plays a club to the king and a club back to the ace, West discarding the 8 of diamonds.

South now leads the 9 of hearts: 2, king, ace. What do you play next?

Answer 43

```
              ♠ A
              ♡ K 8 6 4 3
              ◊ J 4 2
              ♣ K Q 10 5

♠ 9 8 6 3          N          ♠ 7 4 2
♡ J 5 2       W         E     ♡ A 10
◊ 9 8 7 6 5        S          ◊ K Q 10 3
♣ 6                          ♣ 8 7 3 2

              ♠ K Q J 10 5
              ♡ Q 9 7
              ◊ A
              ♣ A J 9 4
```

South, who has bid spades and clubs and shown some support for hearts, plays in six clubs. West leads the ◊8, covered by the jack, queen and ace. Declarer takes two rounds of trumps, West discarding the ◊ 6, then leads the ♡9 to the 2, king and ace.

South appears to have fine spades and yet never attempted to get rid of any of dummy's diamonds. This, combined with the bidding, points to South being 5-3-1-4. Even if his spades are solid and he holds the queen of hearts, he will need a diamond ruff in his own hand for a twelfth trick. So long as you return a heart now, he will have insoluble entry problems. If you play anything else, such as a trump, he will take the diamond ruff, cross to ♠A, draw trumps, and enter his hand with the queen of hearts.

44. Turn and Twist

Dealer North   E-W vulnerable

<pre>
                    ♠ Q 9 7
                    ♡ 10 8 7 3 2
                    ◇ —
                    ♣ Q 9 7 5 2

    ♠ 5 3
    ♡ Q J 9   N
    ◇ Q 8 7 4   W   E
    ♣ A K J 3   S
</pre>

South	West	North	East
—	—	Pass	1◇
2♠	3♠	4♠	6◇
Pass	Pass	6♠	Double
Pass	Pass	Pass	

It is quite possible that East is playing on the nerves of the nonvulnerable opponents, knowing that they are likely to sacrifice. But now, playing in a pair game, you must aim at 800, so that you will obtain a better score than those who bid and make five diamonds your way.

On your lead of the king of clubs East plays the 8 and declarer the 10. How do you continue?

Answer 44

♠ Q 9 7
♡ 10 8 7 3 2
◊ —
♣ Q 9 7 5 2

♠ 5 3   ♠ 6 2
♡ Q J 9   ♡ A K 4
◊ Q 8 7 4   ◊ A K 10 6 5 3
♣ A K J 3   ♣ 8 4

♠ A K J 10 8 4
♡ 6 5
◊ J 9 2
♣ 10 6

Energetic bidding by East has driven the opposition into a phantom sacrifice of six spades over six diamonds. However, this tactical success may be a phantom for your side unless you can obtain a penalty of 800.

After the king of clubs has held the first trick, partner playing the 8, you have four possible lines of attack:

      1. Continue clubs, playing partner for a singleton. In this case declarer will be short in hearts and you won't take five tricks.

      2. Switch to a trump. Declarer will win and lead a club; again, you won't win five tricks.

      3. Attack hearts. The danger now is that, with hearts breaking 3-3, declarer will establish long hearts in dummy.

      4. Shorten the dummy by leading a diamond.

It is usually right to attack entries in the hand that has length in a side suit, and a diamond at trick two in fact holds South to eight tricks. Whether he exits from dummy with a heart or a club, you will lead a trump when next in and, turn and twist as he may, South will be held to six trumps and two ruffs, or their equivalent.

Even one round of hearts before the diamond would be a mistake, enabling the declarer to play for tricks in hearts.

45. Strike First

Dealer South   N-S vulnerable

♠ K J 7 4 2
♡ 8 5 4
♦ 3
♣ A K 10 7

♡ 3 led

♠ Q 9 6 3
♡ A Q J 10 9
♦ 6
♣ 9 6 2

South	West	North	East
1♣	Pass	1♠	2♡
3♦	Pass	4♣	Pass
4♦	Pass	5♦	Pass
Pass	Double	Pass	Pass

North-South are playing a one club system. North's response of one spade promised a minimum of 8 points and a 5-card suit. The rest of the bidding was on natural lines.

West leads the 3 of hearts, you win with the ace and South follows with the 2. You would expect your partner to lead low from three small or three to an honor in your suit. What do you lead at trick two?

Answer 45

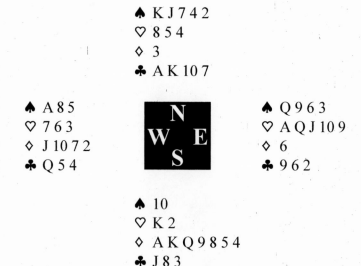

```
                    ♠ K J 7 4 2
                    ♡ 8 5 4
                    ◊ 3
                    ♣ A K 10 7
  ♠ A 8 5                            ♠ Q 9 6 3
  ♡ 7 6 3          N                 ♡ A Q J 10 9
  ◊ J 10 7 2     W   E               ◊ 6
  ♣ Q 5 4          S                 ♣ 9 6 2
                    ♠ 10
                    ♡ K 2
                    ◊ A K Q 9 8 5 4
                    ♣ J 8 3
```

South plays in five diamonds, doubled by West, after East has overcalled in hearts. West leads the ♡3 to his partner's ace and South follows with the 2.

West would not have doubled on the strength of K x x in his partner's suit. It is also unlikely that he would have doubled with a singleton heart and a trump trick, because his partner might not hold the ace of hearts. On all grounds, the reason for the double is likely to be that he has two tricks in the trump suit or the spade ace and one trump trick.

You can not cater to both. If you play a spade and declarer holds: A, K2 AKJ9854, J83, he can use dummy's three club entries to ruff a heart and two spades and end play your partner in trump.

On the other hand, if you lead a club now before the major suits are unblocked, you can prevent the end play. But, with the cards as they actually lie, declarer can draw three trump and throw his losing spade on the fourth round of clubs.

When two possible defenses present themselves, take the simpler road. Lead a spade.

46 Pencil and Paper

Dealer South   N-S vulnerable

<pre>
                        ♠ K 7 6
                        ♡ K
                        ◊ J 10 5 3
                        ♣ A 9 7 4 2
</pre>

<pre>
    ♠ 10 8
    ♡ A Q 9 5 3
    ◊ K 9 6 2
    ♣ 8 3
</pre>

South	West	North	East
1◊	1♡	4◊	4♡
5◊	Double	Pass	Pass
Pass			

You were pleased to be able to double five diamonds before partner could do anything foolish. The game must be to weaken the declarer's trump holding, so you begin with ace of hearts and a low heart. Dummy ruffs and your partner completes an echo, signifying an even number. On the jack of diamonds your partner discards the ♣K and you hold off. South crosses to the ♠A, partner playing the 4, ruffs his third heart, and runs the ◊10, on which East discards his last heart.

It's not going to be easy to beat this contract, after all. Construct partner's likely hand before deciding what to do.

Answer 46

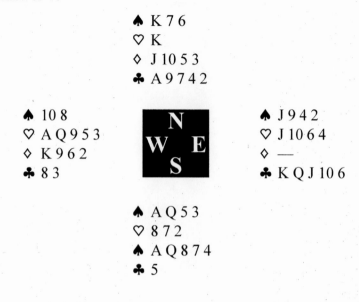

♠ K 7 6
♥ K
♦ J 10 5 3
♣ A 9 7 4 2

♠ 10 8
♥ A Q 9 5 3
♦ K 9 6 2
♣ 8 3

♠ J 9 4 2
♥ J 10 6 4
♦ —
♣ K Q J 10 6

♠ A Q 5 3
♥ 8 7 2
♠ A Q 8 7 4
♣ 5

Playing in five diamonds doubled, South ruffs the second heart, runs the ♦J, crosses to the ♠A to ruff another heart, and runs the ♦10. Partner has played all his hearts and has signaled with the king of clubs.

It is not difficult to read partner for ♠J x x x; if he had held ♠ Q x x x he would have completed an echo when the second trump was led. South appears to have ten tricks on top, by way of four diamonds, three spades, two ruffs and a club.

Can you save East from being squeezed in spades and clubs? If you win with the ♦K, a spade is the best card of exit. South can still succeed if he wins with ♠Q and plays off two top trumps. East is caught in a trump squeeze.

If you take your time and consider all the possibilities, you will come to the conclusion that by winning with the ♦K you improve the timing for a squeeze. So try the effect of holding off. The declarer may play a spade to the queen, or king and a spade to the queen, or try ace and another club, but in all cases he will fail. You don't need to work out these endings; it is sufficient to realize that if you take the ♦K your partner will be squeezed.

47. Small Deception

Dealer South   Neither side vulnerable

<pre>
                        ♠ 10 7 5 2
                        ♡ 8 6
                        ◊ Q J 10 8 6 2
                        ♣ 9

     ♠ A J 4
     ♡ Q 10 7 5 2   N
     ◊ 7   W   E
     ♣ 10 8 7 6   S
</pre>

South	West	North	East
2NT	Pass	3NT	Pass
Pass	Pass		

Some players would look for a possible fit in spades over 2NT, but (*a*) the odds are against partner holding four spades, (*b*) such inquiries tend to be helpful to the defense, and (c) even if partner does hold four spades it is by no means certain that four spades will be a better contract than 3NT.

You lead the 5 of hearts against 3NT, East plays the 9 and South wins with the king. South leads the ace of diamonds, East playing the 3, and follows with the 5 of diamonds. How do you play to this trick?

Answer 47

<pre>
                    ♠ 10 7 5 2
                    ♡ 8 6
                    ◊ Q J 10 8 6 2
                    ♣ 9
</pre>

<pre>
  ♠ A J 4   ♠ Q 9 6 3
  ♡ Q 10 7 5 2   ♡ 9 4 3
  ◊ 7   ◊ K 3
  ♣ 10 8 7 6   ♣ Q J 5 4
</pre>

<pre>
                    ♠ K 8
                    ♡ A K J
                    ◊ A 9 5 4
                    ♣ A K 3 2
</pre>

Defending against 3NT, you lead the 5 of hearts. This is covered by the 9 and king. South then plays ace and another diamond.

The first thing you should have noted is that declarer has practiced a small deception in hearts. Partner, holding the jack, would not have played the 9 on the first trick.

No doubt South is hoping for another heart from the defense, and will then run nine tricks. There is no hope in clubs, but perhaps South has just K x or Q x in spades?

How will you suggest a spade switch to your partner? The 6 of clubs would not be clear, and the 2 of hearts might suggest a switch to clubs. The card to play, both to illuminate the heart position and for suit-preference, is the *queen* of hearts.

48. Vain Contention

Dealer North Neither side vulnerable

♠ 7 6 3
♡ J 8 7 2
♢ A Q 6 5
♣ A 9

♠ A K 8 5
♡ 10 5
♢ 10 4
♣ K 7 6 3 2

South	West	North	East
—	—	Pass	Pass
1♠	Pass	2NT	Pass
3♡	Pass	4♡	Pass
Pass	Pass		

The response to one spade, by a passed hand, is awkward unless special conventions are in use.

Realizing that there might be a chance for a spade ruff, West, at rubber bridge, led the king of spades, on which East dropped the 4 and declarer the 9. What should West play next?

Answer 48

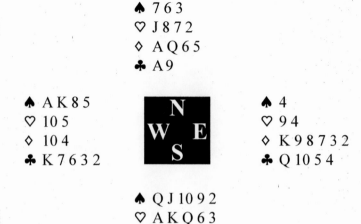

```
              ♠ 7 6 3
              ♡ J 8 7 2
              ◇ A Q 6 5
              ♣ A 9

  ♠ A K 8 5                    ♠ 4
  ♡ 10 5           N          ♡ 9 4
  ◇ 10 4        W     E       ◇ K 9 8 7 3 2
  ♣ K 7 6 3 2      S          ♣ Q 10 5 4

              ♠ Q J 10 9 2
              ♡ A K Q 6 3
              ◇ J
              ♣ J 8
```

South played in four hearts after he had opened one spade and North had responded 2NT. As there were chances for a spade ruff, West led the king of spades, on which East played the 4 and declarer the 9. Pleased with his acumen, West continued with ace and another spade. East ruffed, but dummy's club loser wept away on a long spade.

'I couldn't do everything,' commented West. 'If I lead a club at trick two we don't get our spade ruff.'

True, but if West has the wit to lead a low spade at trick two, East can ruff and return a club while West still has the ace of spades. It is generally right to retain the primary control in declarer's side suit.

49. Legal Eagle

Dealer North   N-S vulnerable

♠ 8 6 3
♡ 6
♢ A J 8 7 6
♣ 10 9 6 4

We have not presented any other lead problems in this book, but opening leads are a very important part of defence, are they not? This one, in which one of the present authors was concerned, had some unusual features. First, the- bidding:

South	West	North	East
—	—	1♠	2♢[1]
2♡	Pass[2]	3♣	Pass
3♢	5♢	5♡	Pass
6♡	Pass	Pass	Pass

1. At this point Eddie Kantar, (East), playing with John Mohan in the Lifemasters' Pairs, unaccountably dropped the ace of clubs on the table. *

2. In accordance with Law 23, West had to pass for one round. The ace of clubs, of course, was an exposed card, and South, exercising one of his options, prohibited a club lead. The penalty card was then picked up and West was free to choose any card except a club. What *did* he choose, and why?

* *I hold so few aces, you'd think I'd hold onto them more tightly.* — E.B.K.

Answer 49

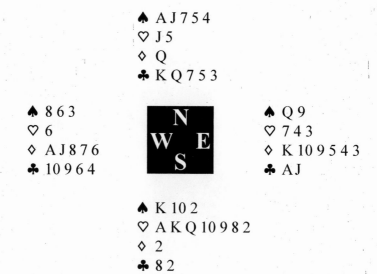

```
              ♠ A J 7 5 4
              ♡ J 5
              ◇ Q
              ♣ K Q 7 5 3

  ♠ 8 6 3                        ♠ Q 9
  ♡ 6                            ♡ 7 4 3
  ◇ A J 8 7 6                    ◇ K 10 9 5 4 3
  ♣ 10 9 6 4                     ♣ A J

              ♠ K 10 2
              ♡ A K Q 10 9 8 2
              ◇ 2
              ♣ 8 2
```

South plays in six hearts after the defenders have bid and supported diamonds. During the auction East has exposed the ace of clubs and South has prohibited a club lead.

(If you turn back, you will see that the North-South bidding was unlifemasterly in several respects.)

Mohan led a *low* diamond. Kantar won with the king and cashed his ace of clubs to defeat the contract.

You see why it was essential to lead a low diamond, not the ace? The prohibition against leading a club exists so long as the lead is retained. If West had led ◇A he would have been unable to lead a club at trick two, and South might have discarded his club losers on dummy's spades.

50. Place Your Money

Dealer South   Both sides vulnerable

          ♠ 4 2
          ♡ 10 4 3
          ◊ A K J 9 8
          ♣ 10 7 2

♠ K 10 8 5 3
♡ K 8
◊ 6 5 3
♣ K 4 3

South	West	North	East
1NT	Pass	3NT	Pass
Pass	Pass		

North-South are playing a strong notrump. You are watching, on Vu-Graph, a match in which the Polish pair, Lebioda and Wilkosz, are East-West. You therefore have the advantage of seeing all the hands.

Wilkosz, West, leads ♠3 (3rd or 5th best) to the jack and ace. South leads ◊10 to the ace, East playing the 4, then runs ♣10, which West wins.

Long pause. 'What do you think he'll lead now?' asks your neighbor. You strike a small bet. Where do you place your money?

Answer 50

```
              ♠ 4 2
              ♡ 10 4 3
              ◇ A K J 9 8
              ♣ 10 7 2

♠ K 10 8 5 3        N          ♠ J 7 6
♡ K 8                          ♡ A Q 7 6 2
◇ 6 5 3      W        E        ◇ 4 2
♣ K 4 3               S        ♣ 8 6 5

              ♠ A Q 9
              ♡ J 9 5
              ◇ Q 10 7
              ♣ A Q J 9
```

South is in 3NT and West leads a low spade, on which East plays |the jack and declarer the ace. South crosses to the ◇A and runs the ♣10 to West's king.

A player who holds an unsupported ace in the suit led will usually hold up the ace, and West may suspect that South has adopted the well-tried ruse of winning with the ace from A Q x, to discourage a shift to hearts. However, this is by no means certain. If the contract is going to depend on the club finesse, South has no reason to hold up the ace of spades from A x or A x x. In that case a switch to hearts might be a major folly.

Wilkosz had it both ways by laying down the king of spades. He trusted his partner, holding Q J x originally, to unblock. When East failed to do this, he shifted resolutely to the king of hearts. So you win the money if you foresaw that his next card would be the king of spades.

51. Time for Reflection

Dealer East E-W vulnerable

```
              ♠ K 8 7 6
              ♡ Q J 9 4 2
              ◇ K
              ♣ K 9 2
```

```
   ◇ A led            ♠ 10 3 2
                      ♡ A 8
                      ◇ Q J 10 8 4 3 2
                      ♣ 3
```

South	West	North	East
—	—	—	3◇
3♠	4◇	4♠	Pass
Pass	Pass		

After his feeble support your partner leads the ace of diamonds. Which diamond do you play on this trick? A low one to signify an odd number? A low one is the hope that partner will take it as suit preference and follow with ace and another club? A high one to induce a heart switch? A middle one to invite a diamond continuation?

Answer 51

```
              ♠ K 8 7 6
              ♡ Q J 9 4 2
              ◇ K
              ♣ K 9 2
♠ 4                          ♠ 10 3 2
♡ K 10 3        N            ♡ A 8
◇ A 6 5     W       E        ◇ Q J 10 8 4 3 2
♣ J 8 7 6 5 4   S            ♣ 3
              ♠ A Q J 9 5
              ♡ 7 6 5
              ◇ 9 7
              ♣ A Q 10
```

South plays in four spades after East has opened with a preemptive three diamonds. West, who has supported diamonds, leads the ace.

East can see two possible ways of beating the contract-a heart ruff if partner has K x x, a club ruff if partner has the ace (or conceivably a singleton ace of spades).

It is not too difficult to combine the possibilities. You issue a decided suit-preference signal with the queen of diamonds. When partner shifts to a heart, the card he chooses will probably reveal whether or not he has the king. If he leads a low heart, return the suit; if a high heart, try a club. (Fortunately, your club is the lowest visible outside the dummy, so partner will not try to give you a heart ruff instead of a club ruff.)

This is not a complicated problem, but it raises another question. It is always embarrassing, after hesitation, to play a card that is intended as suit-preference but might (not in this example) be otherwise interpreted. The solution is *always* to pause for a while after the dummy has gone down; it's good for your bridge, too.

52.Evasive Action

Dealer East   N-S vulnerable

           ♠ 8 5 3
           ♡ A 10 6
           ◇ K Q J 5 3
           ♣ A Q

♠ 4
♡ Q 3
◇ 9 8 6 4
♣ K J 9 8 5 3

After two passes you open as West with a semi-psychic one club. The bidding continues:

South	West	North	East
Pass	Pass	1♣	1NT
2♠	Double	3♣	Pass
Pass	3♡	Pass	4♡
Pass	Pass	Pass	

You lead your singleton spade. East wins with the ace and returns the queen, which is covered by South's king. How do you plan the defense?

Answer 52

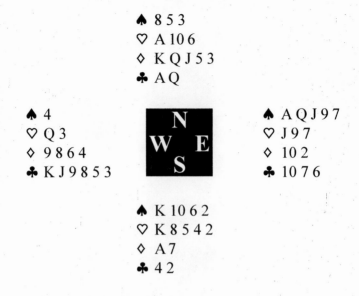

```
                    ♠ 8 5 3
                    ♡ A 10 6
                    ◇ K Q J 5 3
                    ♣ A Q

♠ 4                                    ♠ A Q J 9 7
♡ Q 3               N                  ♡ J 9 7
◇ 9 8 6 4       W       E              ◇ 10 2
♣ K J 9 8 5 3       S                  ♣ 10 7 6

                    ♠ K 10 6 2
                    ♡ K 8 5 4 2
                    ◇ A 7
                    ♣ 4 2
```

Defending against four hearts, you lead a spade to the ace, and East's return of the queen is covered by the king. No doubt partner has a spade to cash, but how will he obtain the lead? Suppose you ruff low and exit with a diamond or a club. When South leads a low trump, and your queen appears, he will let it hold; end of defense.

You can defeat the declarer's avoidance play by ruffing with the *queen* at trick two. Note that the same type of play would be right if you held Kx instead of Qx; then ruffing with the king would establish an entry for a partner who might hold either Qx or J 9 x.

53. No Future

Dealer South   Both sides vulnerable

♠ 10 8 6 4
♡ 6 5 2
◇ A K 4 2
♣ K 9

◇ 6 led

♠ A J 9 2
♡ 10 8 3
◇ Q 7
♣ 7 6 4 3

South	West	North	East
1♣	Pass	1◇	Pass
1♡	Pass	1♠	Pass
2NT	Pass	3NT	Pass
Pass	Pass		

North's one spade on the second round is 'fourth suit', suggesting some values in spades but not necessarily a biddable suit.

West leads the 6 of diamonds. After routine examination South plays low from dummy. You win with the queen and South follows with the 3. What do you play now?

Answer 53

♠ 10 8 6 4
♡ 6 5 2
◊ A K 4 2
♣ K 9

♠ 7 5 3   ♠ A J 9 2
♡ A J 7   ♡ 10 8 3
◊ J 9 8 6 5   ◊ Q 7
♣ 10 5   ♣ 7 6 4 3

♠ K Q
♡ K Q 9 4
◊ 10 3
♣ A Q J 8 2

South plays in 3NT after bidding clubs and hearts. West leads the 6 of diamonds and East wins with the queen. What should he return?

This is not a difficult problem if you remember the bidding, but it proved a blind spot for several defenders in a pairs contest.

There is not much future in returning partner's suit. Declarer will win in dummy and lead a heart. It is unlikely that West will have two entries and be allowed to run his diamonds.

There is a good chance, however, that South will hold only two spades. If that is the case, ace and another spade will establish three spade winners for the defense, assuming that West has just one quick entry.

South was wrong to duck the first diamond—but you won't win at this game unless you take advantage of your opponents' mistakes.

54. Sole Concern

Dealer South   Neither side vulnerable

$$\spadesuit \ A\ Q\ 10\ 7\ 6\ 2$$
$$\heartsuit \ 8\ 4$$
$$\diamond \ 9\ 5\ 2$$
$$\clubsuit \ Q\ 3$$

♣ A led

$$\spadesuit \ K\ 5$$
$$\heartsuit \ J\ 3$$
$$\diamond \ Q\ 7\ 6\ 3$$
$$\clubsuit \ K\ J\ 7\ 5\ 4$$

South	West	North	East
1♡	Pass	1♠	Pass
3◊	Pass	3♠	Pass
4◊	Pass	5◊	Pass
Pass	Pass		

North's five diamonds is not well judged: he should aim for ten tricks in hearts rather than eleven in diamonds.

Your partner leads the ace of clubs and follows with the 2, South playing the 6 and 9 on the first two tricks. What do you lead at trick three?

Answer 54

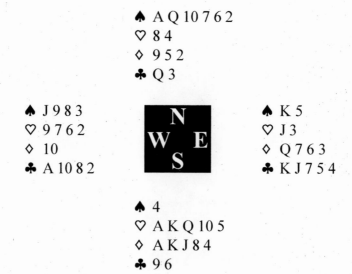

♠ A Q 10 7 6 2
♡ 8 4
◊ 9 5 2
♣ Q 3

♠ J 9 8 3
♡ 9 7 6 2
◊ 10
♣ A 10 8 2

♠ K 5
♡ J 3
◊ Q 7 6 3
♣ K J 7 5 4

♠ 4
♡ A K Q 10 5
◊ A K J 8 4
♣ 9 6

Having shown a red two-suiter, South plays in five diamonds. Your partner leads the ace of clubs and you win the second trick with the king.

At this point your sole concern is to protect your possible trump trick. Suppose you make a neutral return, such as a heart. When South sees the 10 (or jack) of diamonds fall under the ace, he may decide to play West for a singleton rather than precisely Q 10 (or QJ). (Also, he must allow for the possibility that West has dropped the 10 from 10x.) So South may cross to dummy and run the 9 of diamonds, picking up your queen. You can forestall this unpleasant sequence by returning a spade at trick three.

There is an interesting corollary to this problem. Suppose you had held x x x in diamonds, declarer A K Q 10 x, and your partner J x. Again, you return a spade into dummy's strong suit. The declarer, if he understands this form of play and thinks that you do too, may conclude that you are attempting to protect a trump holding of J x x x and may therefore finesse the 10 on the first round.

55. Open Invitation

Dealer South Neither side vulnerable

♠ A K 10
♡ K J 7
◇ Q J 4
♣ K J 10 9

♡ 6 led

♠ 8 6 4 2
♡ A 3
◇ 8 7 6 3
♣ A Q 4

South	West	North	East
Pass	Pass	1♣	Pass
2NT	Pass	3NT	Pass
Pass	Pass		

Playing in a pairs event, you think you have a chance to qualify, but you cannot afford a bad result on the last round. On West's lead of the 6 of hearts the 7 is played from dummy. Judging the lead to be second best from a weak suit, you play the 3, declining to part with the ace. South wins with the 10 and leads the 5 of clubs, on which West plays the 7 and dummy the 9. How do you plan the defense?

Answer 55

<pre>
              ♠ A K 10
              ♡ K J 7
              ◇ Q J 4
              ♣ K J 10 9

  ♠ J 7 5   N   ♠ 8 6 4 2
  ♡ 9 6 5 4 2   ♡ A 3
  ◇ 9 5 2   W   E   ◇ 8 7 6 3
  ♣ 7 3   S   ♣ A Q 4

              ♠ Q 9 3
              ♡ Q 10 8
              ◇ A K 10
              ♣ 8 6 5 2
</pre>

South plays in 3NT and West leads the ♡6. As East, you hold up the ace. Declarer wins with the 8 and leads a club to the jack.

In view of the strength of the dummy, the most that partner can hold is one jack. You can supply three tricks and must aim for a fourth. This is vital, because at other tables a spade or diamond might be led, giving the defense time to establish a long card.

As it is, you must enlist some aid from the declarer. You must duck the club—and quickly! Declarer may then be tempted to return to hand with a diamond or a spade for another club lead. Now you will have time to establish a thirteenth diamond or spade before South can arrive at a tenth trick.

56. Stunned

Dealer South   Neither side vulnerable

```
              ♠ 10 8 5
              ♡ Q 7 3
              ◊ K 9 6 4
              ♣ Q J 5
♠ A Q
♡ K J 9 6 5 2
◊ 7 3
♣ A 6 2
```

South	West	North	East
1♠	2♡	2♠	Pass
Pass	3♡	Pass	Pass
3♠	Pass	Pass	Pass

Your intrepid three hearts has achieved its object of pushing your opponents to the three level. Can you profit from this? Your lead of the 7 of diamonds is won by dummy's king, partner playing low. South leads the 8 of spades from dummy and runs it, partner playing -the 7. What now?

Answer 56

<pre>
              ♠ 10 8 5
              ♡ Q 7 3
              ◊ K 9 6 4
              ♣ Q J 5

♠ A Q   ♠ 7 6 2
♡ K J 9 6 5 2   ♡ 10
◊ 7 3   ◊ Q J 10 5 2
♣ A 6 2   ♣ 10 8 7 3

              ♠ K J 9 4 3
              ♡ A 8 4
              ◊ A 8
              ♣ K 9 4
</pre>

Defending against three spades, you lead the 7 of diamonds. This is won on the table and declarer runs the 8 of spades to your queen, partner playing the 7.

It looks as though partner's 7 of spades is the beginning of a trump echo. There are some foolish players who echo in trumps whenever they have three. The echo should also indicate the desire to trump a side suit. Thus, partner seems to be inviting a heart switch.

The jack of hearts will accomplish nothing, as dummy will win with the queen and East will be ruffing a loser on the next round. But if East's singleton is the 10 and you lead the king now, then the jack of hearts, when you come in with the ace of spades, will strike a stunning blow.

57. Rare Mistake

Dealer South   Neither side vulnerable

♠ J 8 7
♡ A 9 8 5 4
♦ 6 3
♣ 7 4 2

♦ Q led   ♠ Q 10 3
♡ K Q 10
♦ A 10 7 4
♣ 10 6 3

South	West	North	East
1♠	Pass	2♠	Pass
4♠	Pass	Pass	Pass

On the lead of the queen of diamonds you play the ace, because declarer might possibly hold a singleton king. In fact, he plays the 5. You make your lead to the second trick, and the contract is eventually made. Nobody notices anything, but it occurs to you later that you made one of your rare mistakes at trick two. What ought you have led ?

Answer 57

<pre>
                  ♠ J 8 7
                  ♡ A 9 8 5 4
                  ◇ 6 3
                  ♣ 7 4 2

    ♠ 9 5   N   ♠ Q 10 3
    ♡ 7 3 2   W   E   ♡ K Q 10
    ◇ Q J 9 2   S   ◇ A 10 7 4
    ♣ Q 9 8 5   ♣ 10 6 3

                  ♠ A K 6 4 2
                  ♡ J 6
                  ◇ K 8 5
                  ♣ A K J
</pre>

West leads the queen of diamonds against four spades and you win with the ace.

Deny it if you wish, but we suspect that you returned a club to the weakness in dummy. Declarer won and ducked a heart. You led a second club and South, believing your partner's signal on the first round, annoyingly went up with the king, cashed the top spades, then played ace of hearts and ruffed a heart. He entered dummy with a diamond ruff and discarded his club loser on a winning heart.

If this is what happened, you failed to realize that your main plan should have been to kill the heart suit as a source of discards. At trick two it was essential to return a diamond. When you come in with a heart you play another diamond, forcing dummy to ruff, and declarer cannot then escape a club loser.

Of course, it is important to watch the spot cards on the second round of diamonds. If partner shows four we'll know we can force the dummy with a diamond. If partner shows five, we'll lead a club and wait for our tricks.

58. Pinned Back

Dealer South   Both sides vulnerable

```
              ♠ Q 8
              ♡ A 4
              ◇ K Q 10 5
              ♣ K Q 6 3 2
```

```
◇ 9 led                        ♠ K 6
                               ♡ K 10 5 3
                               ◇ A J 8 6
                               ♣ 9 7 4
```

South	West	North	East
1♠	Pass	2♣	Pass
2♠	Pass	4♠	Pass
Pass	Pass		

Partner's lead of the 9 of diamonds is covered by the queen. Since partner can hardly have a quick entry, there is no point in retaining a major tenace. You win with the ace and declarer plays the 3. West would not lead the 9 from a holding such as 972, so probably he has a doubleton. You are playing in a pairs event. South is a player with a big reputation and you would dearly love to pin his ears back. How do you defend?

Answer 58

                    ♠ Q 8
                    ♡ A 4
                    ◇ K Q 10 5
                    ♣ K Q 6 3 2

♠ 7 5 3   ♠ K 6
♡ J 9 7 6 2   ♡ K 10 5 3
◇ 9 4   ◇ A J 8 6
♣ J 8 5   ♣ 9 7 4

                    ♠ A J 10 9 4 2
                    ♡ Q 8
                    ◇ 7 3 2
                    ♣ A 10

South is in four spades and West leads the 9 of diamonds. Dummy plays the queen and you win with the ace.

You cannot hope to defeat four spades, but an imaginative stroke may hold the declarer to 620, while at all other tables the score will be 650 or 680.

The declarer must hold the ace of clubs, and if his spades are headed by A J 10 he threatens to run twelve tricks. However, you can introduce a diversion by returning the *jack* of diamonds at trick two. Fearing a diamond ruff, South may refuse the trump finesse. He will be greatly discomfited when your partner ruffs the third round of diamonds.

59. Not by Force

Dealer North   N-S vulnerable

$\quad\quad\quad\quad\quad$ ♠ 9 2
$\quad\quad\quad\quad\quad$ ♡ A Q J 10
$\quad\quad\quad\quad\quad$ ◊ A Q 10
$\quad\quad\quad\quad\quad$ ♣ K Q J 3

♠ K Q 10 7 6 5
♡ K 7
◊ J 5 4 3
♣ 7

South	West	North	East
—	—	1♣	Pass
1NT	2♠	3♠	Pass
3NT	Pass	Pass	Pass

You lead the king of spades, on which East plays the 3 and declarer the 4. You would expect your partner to unblock the jack from J x and to play the middle card from J x x. The natural conclusion is that declarer has ♠AJ4. What do you do next?

Answer 59

$\spadesuit$ 9 2
$\heartsuit$ A Q J 10
$\diamondsuit$ A Q 10
$\clubsuit$ K Q J 3

$\spadesuit$ K Q 10 7 6 5
$\heartsuit$ K 7
$\diamondsuit$ J 5 4 3
$\clubsuit$ 7

$\spadesuit$ 8 3
$\heartsuit$ 8 6 4 2
$\diamondsuit$ 9 6 2
$\clubsuit$ A 9 8 4

$\spadesuit$ A J 4
$\heartsuit$ 9 5 3
$\diamondsuit$ K 8 7
$\clubsuit$ 10 6 5 2

Defending against 3NT, after South has responded 1 NT to one club, you lead the king of spades. When partner drops the 3 and declarer the 4, you assume that South began with AJ4. You would like to put partner in to return a spade through the AJ, but you can credit East with only one of the high cards, king of diamonds or ace of clubs. To find East with the king of diamonds will not help, because South, with $\clubsuit$A, will have ample tricks. And to lead a club won't help either, because again the declarer can hardly fail, needing just one finesse in hearts to make four tricks in the suit.

When you cannot defeat a contract by force, you must consider the chances of a bluff. You must use a little imagination and lead the 7 of hearts at trick two, without too much ponderous thought. Placing East with $\heartsuit$K and West with $\clubsuit$A, South will probably go up with the ace of hearts and lead a club. Then eight tricks will be his limit.

60. Not Embarrassed

Dealer North E-W vulnerable

              ♠ A J 7 6 5 4
              ♡ K 7 5
              ◊ 2
              ♣ K 8 5

  ♠ 2 led   ♠ K Q 9 8
                   ♡ 9 8 6
                                       ◊ 4 3
                                       ♣ A J 6 4

South	West	North	East
—	—	1♠	Pass
3◊	Pass	3♠	Pass
4◊	Pass	5◊	Pass
5♡	Pass	5♠	Pass
6♣	Pass	6◊	Pass
Pass	Pass		

As usual, you have cut the worst player at the rubber bridge table and you have a suspicion that the somewhat involved auction is intended to confuse him. However, the general position soon becomes clear. Declarer wins the spade lead in dummy, draws two trumps, on which your partner plays the 9 and 10, then runs the 10 of spades to your queen, West discarding the 7 of clubs. Is there anything you can do to preserve your lead in this uneven contest?

Answer 60

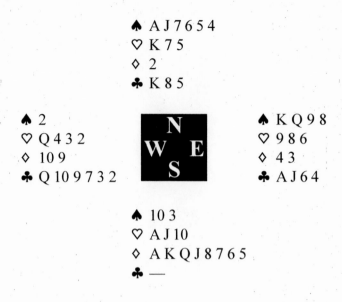

```
              ♠ A J 7 6 5 4
              ♡ K 7 5
              ◊ 2
              ♣ K 8 5

  ♠ 2                              ♠ K Q 9 8
  ♡ Q 4 3 2          N            ♡ 9 8 6
  ◊ 10 9         W       E        ◊ 4 3
  ♣ Q 10 9 7 3 2     S            ♣ A J 6 4

              ♠ 10 3
              ♡ A J 10
              ◊ A K Q J 8 7 6 5
              ♣ —
```

Playing in six diamonds, South wins the spade lead in dummy, draws trumps, and runs the♠ 10 to the queen, West discarding the ♣ 7.

It is easy to place declarer with a void in clubs, so probably you thought of returning a low club. Yes, but why?

The answer is that if South reads West for the ace of clubs his thoughts will turn at once to a double squeeze. East is known to hold the spade control, West is assumed to hold ♣ A in front of dummy's king, so why risk a heart finesse? South will reduce to a position where he holds ♡A J 10 and 0 5, while dummy has ♠J, ♡K 7 and ♣ K.

When he leads his last diamond, South will be disturbed to see West discard the queen of clubs, not an embarrassed heart. He will try the jack of hearts next, and you will die a thousand deaths while West pulls out the queen of hearts, puts it back, pulls it out . . .

61. Student Power

Dealer West   Neither side vulnerable

 ♠ J 10 5
 ♡ Q J 10 9 8 2
 ◊ A 6 2
 ♣ 4

♠ K 9 8 4 2
♡ K 5
◊ J 7 5
♣ A 7 3

South	West	North	East
—	Pass	Pass*	Pass
1◊	1♠	2♡	Pass
3NT	Pass	Pass	Pass

*not playing weak twos

A disheveled young man comes to your table and says breezily, 'Hallo, I've read your book.' Having written more than one book, you resent this remark and nod coldly.

A minute or two later you decide, despite South's 3NT, to lead from your long suit. Dummy plays the ♠5, partner the 7 and declarer the queen. South follows with the ace of hearts, then K Q of diamonds and a diamond to the ace, partner discarding a heart. Declarer then leads the queen of hearts from dummy and jettisons the ace of spades! Yes, he's been reading books all right. Can you produce a counterstroke?

Answer 61

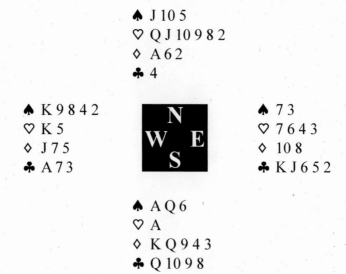

♠ J 10 5
♡ Q J 10 9 8 2
◇ A 6 2
♣ 4

♠ K 9 8 4 2   ♠ 7 3
♡ K 5   ♡ 7 6 4 3
◇ J 7 5   ◇ 10 8
♣ A 7 3   ♣ K J 6 5 2

♠ A Q 6
♡ A
◇ K Q 9 4 3
♣ Q 10 9 8

Playing in 3NT, South wins the spade lead with the queen, cashes the ♡A, plays three top diamonds, finishing in dummy, then leads the ♡Q and discards the ace of spades.

At least you know what is happening. South must be 3-1-5-4, because if he had started with four spades he would .have established a ninth trick by conceding a spade to the king.

You can still beat the contract if partner's clubs are as good as K J x x x or K 10 9 x x. You must cash the king of spades, then lead the ace of clubs, followed by the 7. So long as partner has the sense to play low, you take three clubs, a heart and a spade. More important, you deprive your brash opponent of the chance to tell how he outwitted you.

62. Lifeline

Dealer North   Neither side vulnerable

                    ♠ 8 4 3
                    ♡ K Q 6
                    ◊ A K
                    ♣ K Q J 9 4

    ♠ A K 7 6
    ♡ 4 2
    ◊ Q 10 7 2
    ♣ 10 8 3

South	West	North	East
—	—	1♣	Pass
1♡	Pass	2NT	Pass
3♡	Pass	Pass	Pass

South's three hearts is a sign-off in the Acol system, and North passes in disciplined fashion.

Sitting West, you lead the king of spades, on which East plays the 2 (count)* and declarer the 10. No doubt partner holds the other two aces, so four tricks are in view. Where will you go for a fifth?

---

* *Many experts play attitude in this situation.*

Answer 62

```
              ♠ 8 4 3
              ♡ K Q 6
              ◊ A K
              ♣ K Q J 9 4

♠ A K 7 6                          ♠ 9 5 2
♡ 4 2         N                    ♡ A J
◊ Q 10 7 2   W   E                 ◊ J 8 6 4 3
♣ 10 8 3        S                  ♣ A 6 5

              ♠ Q J 10
              ♡ 10 9 8 7 5 3
              ◊ 9 5
              ♣ 7 2
```

Defending against three hearts, you lead the king of spades, on which partner plays the 2 (count) and declarer the 10. To beat the contract, you will need to make three spades and two aces, or two spades, two aces and an extra trump trick. If partner holds Q x x in spades it will do no harm to lead a *low* spade at trick two. This gains when, as in the diagram, East holds three spades and A J of hearts. When he comes in with the ace of hearts (or the ace of clubs) he will return a spade, and a fourth spade will promote a trick for the jack of hearts.

It is true that you could also play partner for Ax of clubs and try for a club ruff. However this is not a promising idea, because if South were 3-6-1-3 he would be able to discard a club on the second round of diamonds.

63. Not in Gath

Dealer South   Neither side vulnerable

$\spadesuit$ A 10 6 5
$\heartsuit$ 8 7 3
$\diamondsuit$ K Q J 3 2
$\clubsuit$ 8

$\spadesuit$ K J 9 8 7 2
$\heartsuit$ J 9 6
$\diamondsuit$ 8 7
$\clubsuit$ A 5

South	West	North	East
1$\clubsuit$	2$\spadesuit$	3$\diamondsuit$	3$\spadesuit$
4$\clubsuit$	Pass	4$\diamondsuit$	Pass
4$\spadesuit$	Pass	5$\diamondsuit$	Pass
6$\clubsuit$	Pass	Pass	Pass

Sitting West, you lead the 8 of diamonds. Your partnership style is to show the count, and partner's card suggests an even number. South wins with the ace of diamonds and leads the king of clubs, which you win, partner playing the 7. What now? You are playing with Belladonna, and you don't want to let him down.

Answer 63

```
                    ♠ A 10 6 5
                    ♡ 8 7 3
                    ◊ K Q J 3 2
                    ♣ 8
```

```
♠ K J 9 8 7 2                          ♠ Q 4 3
♡ J 9 6            N                    ♡ A 10 5
◊ 8 7          W       E                ◊ 9 6 5 4
♣ A 5              S                    ♣ 10 7 3
```

```
                    ♠ —
                    ♡ K Q 4 2
                    ◊ A 10
                    ♣ K Q J 9 6 4 2
```

South plays in six clubs after an auction in which East has supported your jump overcall in spades.

In a world championship match between Italy and the Far East, Pittala led the 8 of diamonds. Belladonna's 4 showed an even number (upside down count) and South won with the ace. South led the king of clubs and West won.

Since East had supported spades, evidently on moderate values, he was marked with three. The diamonds were obviously 5-4-2-2. Instead of leading a nervous heart, Pittala cut the communications by leading a second diamond. The declarer's best chance to save a trick from the wreckage was to discard a heart on the ace of spades and play East for a doubleton ace of hearts. East could afford to duck when a heart was led from dummy, so the contract was defeated by two tricks.

Tell it not in Gath, but in another match the Brazilian West led a spade against the same contract of six clubs and, when in with the ♣A, tried a diamond!

64. Dilemma

Dealer South   N-S vulnerable

                    ♠ Q J 9 7
                     ♡ K 10 4
                     ◊ 8 7 6
                     ♣ K J 9

                                        ♠ 3 2
♣ 10 led   ♡ Q 8 5
                                        ◊ Q J 10
                                        ♣ A 8 6 5 3

South	West	North	East
1◊	2♡	2NT	3♡
3♠	Pass	4♠.	Pass
Pass	Pass		

Two hearts is an opening hand with a long suit and North's 2NT is non-forcing.

In a team game West leads the 10 of clubs and the jack is played from dummy. First question: do you duck or do you win? If you win, what do you do next? It is a familiar dilemma, and if you make the wrong play, as opposed to the wrong guess, your partner is the sort of player who will track it down.

Answer 64

```
              ♠ Q J 9 7
              ♡ K 10 4
              ◊ 8 7 6
              ♣ K J 9

♠ K 5 4          N          ♠ 3 2
♡ A K J 9 7 6 2  W   E      ♡ Q 8 5
◊ 5 3 2          S          ◊ Q J 10
♣ 10                        ♣ A 8 6 5 3

              ♠ A 10 8 6
              ♡ 3
              ◊ A K 9 4
              ♣ Q 7 4 2
```

South, who has opened one diamond, finishes in four spades after West has made a jump overcall in hearts. West leads the ♣10 and the jack is played from dummy.

Should East play his partner for a singleton club, or should he duck the first trick, playing partner for a doubleton club and A x x or K x x in spades?

In this type of position you sometimes have to guess, but on the present occasion there is a logical answer. Suppose that partner has a doubleton club. In this case the declarer will not be able to discard a diamond from dummy, and in due course your side will make two aces, a diamond, and a trick in spades (or possibly two tricks in diamonds and none in spades). But if partner has a singleton club, then you must win with the ace and give him the ruff at once.

You don't know about the singleton club, but you do know that winning with the ace and returning a club is most unlikely to cost the contract.

65. Through the Slips

Dealer North   E-W vulnerable

♠ Q 10 6
♡ 8 5 4 2
◊ A Q
♣ K Q 7 3

♠ 8 5 2
♡ A K J 6
◊ K 7
♣ J 8 6 4

South	West	North	East
—	—	1♣	Pass
1♠	Pass	1NT	Pass
3♠	Pass	4♠	Pass
Pass	Pass		

South's three spades is non-forcing. Sitting West, you lead the king of hearts, on which your partner plays the 10 and declarer the 7. It is rubber bridge, and whether your partner would play the 10 from Q 10 x(x), giving attitude rather than count is something you have not discussed. What do you lead at trick two?

Answer 65

```
              ♠ Q 10 6
              ♡ 8 5 4 2
              ◇ A Q
              ♣ K Q 7 3

  ♠ 8 5 2          N          ♠ A
  ♡ A K J 6                   ♡ 10 3
  ◇ K 7        W     E        ◇ 10 8 6 5 4 2
  ♣ J 8 6 4        S          ♣ 10 9 5 2

              ♠ K J 9 7 4 3
              ♡ Q 9 7
              ◇ J 9 3
              ♣ A
```

It is annoying to let a game slip through when your side holds four immediate winners, but it can easily happen on a deal such as this.

Defending against four spades, West led the king of hearts. When his partner dropped the 10 he continued with ace and another—but alas, East could ruff only with the ace of trumps.

West can expect to defeat the contract only if the defense can take three tricks in hearts and an ace. If partner has the ace of clubs, the heart tricks won't run away. If he has the ace of spades it will surely be a singleton (South having made a jump rebid), so the right switch at trick two is a trump. It is somehow difficult to look for partner's entry in the trump suit, and that is why the defense on such hands is often missed.

66. Spoil-sport

Dealer South   Both sides vulnerable

♠ K J 9
♡ A Q 10 3 2
◇ 10 9 4
♣ A 5

♣ 7 led

♠ Q 10
♡ J 9 8 7 6
◇ 8 6 2
♣ 10 4 3

South	West	North	East
1♠	Pass	2♡	Pass
3◇	Pass	3♠	Pass
4◇	Pass	4♡	Pass
4♠	Pass	6♠	Pass
Pass	Pass		

Expert opponents bid to a slam with calm authority on the second board of a national final. When the dummy goes down, you don't think you will be called upon to do anything difficult, but you soon find yourself in the hot seat.

Partner's lead of the 7 of clubs runs to the 10 and jack. South cashes the king of hearts, on which partner plays the 4, then leads a low spade to dummy's jack and your queen. What do you play now?

Answer 66

```
              ♠ K J 9
              ♡ A Q 10 3 2
              ◇ 10 9 4
              ♣ A 5

♠ 7 3 2          N          ♠ Q 10
♡ 5 4       W        E      ♡ J 9 8 7 6
◇ Q 5            S          ◇ 8 6 2
♣ Q 9 8 7 6 2              ♣ 10 4 3

              ♠ A 8 6 5 4
              ♡ K
              ◇ A K J 7 3
              ♣ K J
```

Playing in six spades after strong bidding, South wins the first trick with the ♣J, cashes the ♡K, and finesses the ♠J, losing to the queen.

Declarer's spades must be A x x x x. If his diamonds are headed by AQ he will always lose to the king. The critical situation will be when he has A K J x x.

Suppose you make a neutral return, such as a diamond. South will win, draw trumps, and play top hearts, followed by a heart ruff. Finding that the hearts are held, he will play off his last trump, discarding a diamond from dummy, then cross to the ace of clubs. Meanwhile, to keep the jack of hearts, you will be forced to part with a diamond. When South leads a diamond from dummy at trick twelve, he will know that your last card is a heart and will refuse the finesse; a typical 'show-up' squeeze.

To spoil this little party (which really is not difficult to foresee), you must return a club when in with ♠Q. By the way, if you got it wrong and tried to give partner a heart ruff because he did not begin an echo from 54, don't try to shift the blame. Why would the declarer play the king from Kx for no reason? And, partner didn't begin an echo in trump.

67. Name the Odds

Dealer East   N-S vulnerable

　　　　　　　　　♠ A 10 5
　　　　　　　　　♡ A 8 7 5 2
　　　　　　　　　◇ 5
　　　　　　　　　♣ Q 9 6 3

♠ Q
♡ K J 10 6
◇ J 6 3 2
♣ K J 10 2

South	West	North	East
—	—	—	3♠
3NT	Pass	Pass	Pass

In reply to a question, North says that he and his partner play double for take-out over a pre-empt and that, so far as he knows, 3NT is 'to play'.

You lead the queen of spades. Dummy plays low, your partner the 6 and declarer the 7. What do you make of it all, and what do you play next?

Answer 67

	♠ A 10 5	
	♡ A 8 7 5 2	
	◊ 5	
	♣ Q 9 6 3	

♠ Q		♠ K J 8 6 4 3 2
♡ K J 10 6	**N**	♡ 9 3
◊ J 6 3 2	**W E**	◊ 4
♣ K J 10 2	**S**	♣ 8 7 5

	♠ 9 7	
	♡ Q 4	
	◊ A K Q 10 9 8 7	
	♣ A 4	

East opens three spades and South overcalls with 3NT, described by his partner as 'natural'. You lead the queen of spades, on which dummy plays the 5, East the 6 and South the 7,.

Pietro Forquet, the Italian champion, realized that South's 3NT had been a gambling effort, no doubt based on a long suit of diamonds. Knowing that the diamonds would not run, he switched to the king of clubs to drive out South's entry card.

South won with the ace of clubs and played four rounds of diamonds. Forquet exited with the jack of clubs and the declarer was held to eight tricks.

The declarer would have done better, of course, to win the first trick with the ace of spades. But, East would have done better to overtake the first spade and switch to a rounded suit.

68. Dubious Asset

Dealer North   E-W vulnerable

♠ A K 4
♡ 5 2
◇ A J 8 4 3 2
♣ K Q

♠ J 9 5
♡ K Q 10 7 6 4 3
◇ 10
♣ 8 2

South	West	North	East
—	—	1◇	Pass
2♣	2♡	2♠	Pass
2NT	Pass	3NT	Pass
Pass	Pass		

Playing in a pair event, you lead the king of hearts. East plays the 9 and South the 8, so it looks as though declarer holds ♡ A J 8. What do you lead at trick two?

Answer 68

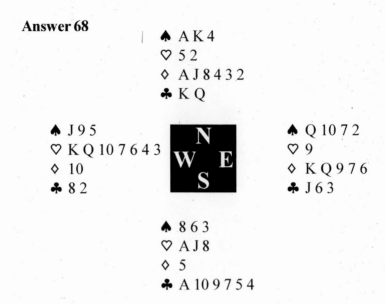

```
                        ♠ A K 4
                        ♡ 5 2
                        ◇ A J 8 4 3 2
                        ♣ K Q

♠ J 9 5                                      ♠ Q 10 7 2
♡ K Q 10 7 6 4 3          N                  ♡ 9
◇ 10                   W     E               ◇ K Q 9 7 6
♣ 8 2                     S                  ♣ J 6 3

                        ♠ 8 6 3
                        ♡ A J 8
                        ◇ 5
                        ♣ A 10 9 7 5 4
```

South, who has responded two clubs to his .partner's one diamond opening, plays in 3NT. West, who has overcalled in hearts, leads the ♡K, which holds the first trick.

The records of this deal in a pairs tournament showed several scores of 630 to South and a number of 950s, at tables where East had ventured a double on the strength of his diamonds. (Note, by the way, that to hold both strength and length in dummy's suit is not always a great asset; it means that the defense will lack communication in the suit.)

When West has won the first trick with the king of hearts, it is somehow difficult to lead into declarer's known ♡A J; but the risk should be taken, because there is a good chance that by removing the declarer's side entry you will kill the club suit. Best, at trick two, is the 10 of hearts, informing partner that he need have no qualms about leading from the queen of spades.

69. Worth Two

Dealer East   Neither side vulnerable

          ♠ A Q 10 9 5 2
          ♡ 3
          ◇ 7 5 4
          ♣ Q 8 3

                                ♠ 8 6 3

◇ K led   ♡ K Q 10 5
                                ◇ A J 8 6
                                ♣ K 4

South	West	North	East
—	—	—	1♡*
Pass	2♡	2♠	Pass
3NT	Pass	Pass	Pass

* One of those Acol four card majors again.

    It's that napkin man again (compare hand 17). You know the analysis will be prolonged, but in the end there will be an instructive point.

    Partner leads the king of diamonds against 3NT; you encourage with the 8, and partner then leads the 2. You are asked to play from this point. What has he in store for you this time?

Answer 69

	♠ A Q 10 9 5 2	
	♡ 3	
	◊ 7 5 4	
	♣ Q 8 3	

♠ 7 4		♠ 8 6 3
♡ 9 4 2	**N**	♡ K Q 10 5
◊ K Q 9 2	**W E**	◊ A J 8 6
♣ J 7 6 5	**S**	♣ K 4

♠ K J
♡ A J 8 7 6
◊ 10 3
♣ A 10 9 2

East has opened one heart, North has intervened in spades, and South has jumped to 3NT. West leads the king of diamonds and follows with the 2.

It is seldom good play, against 3NT, to cash four defensive winners at the beginning of the play. If you do that here, South will cash the ace of hearts and run the spades, squeezing you in hearts and clubs.

So you probably thought of switching to the king of hearts after the second round of diamonds. That's not quite good enough, either. Your last four cards, after the spades have been run, will be ♡Q, ◊J and ♣K4. You will discover, if you work it out, that because both defenders need to keep two clubs, declarer will be able to make the contract by exiting with a diamond.

The very best defense is to win with the jack of diamonds, cash the ace (giving partner no chance to cross your plan), and then lead a heart. The difference is that dummy's exit card, the third diamond, has been removed. A valuable lesson, well worth a napkin, or even two.

70. Clever Stroke

Dealer South   Both sides vulnerable

          ♠ 10 7
          ♡ A 7 4
          ◊ Q 8 5
          ♣ K 10 7 6 3

♠ A 9 4
♡ J 8 5 3
◊ J 7 4 2
♣ A 5

South	West	North	East
1NT	Pass	3NT	Pass
Pass	Pass		

North-South are playing a 15-17 notrump.

For no better reason than that you cannot make up your mind between the red suits, you decide to lead the 4 of spades. This seems to turn out quite well when East wins with the queen and returns the 5. South follows with the 2 and the jack. After winning with the ace, how do you continue?

Answer 70

```
              ♠ 10 7
              ♡ A 7 4
              ◇ Q 8 5
              ♣ K 10 7 6 3
```

```
♠ A 9 4                      ♠ K Q 6 5 3
♡ J 8 5 3        N           ♡ 9 6 2
◇ J 7 4 2     W     E        ◇ 10 9 3
♣ A 5           S            ♣ 8 4
```

```
              ♠ J 8 2
              ♡ K Q 10
              ◇ A K 6
              ♣ Q J 9 2
```

It is not easy to judge what this problem is about until you see what happened at the table.

Defending against 3NT, West led the 4 of spades to his partner's queen, and East returned the 5. On this trick a resourceful declarer played the jack. When West then led the 9, East had to allow for the possibility that his partner had led from A 9 8 x, and accordingly ducked. End of story!

West, having made an unusual lead, might have foreseen this possibility. It would have been a master stroke to cash the ace of clubs before leading the third spade. Then East would know that the contract could be defeated whether his partner had led from A 9 x or A 9 8 x. Taking no chances, he would overtake the 9 of spades.

71. Entry Permit

Dealer North   Neither side vulnerable

♠ Q 8
♡ Q 7 4
◇ A K
♣ A J 10 8 6 4

♡ 9 led

♠ J 9 5 2
♡ A J 10 6 3
◇ Q 5
♣ Q 2

South	West	North	East
—	—	1♣	1♡
1NT	Pass	3NT	Pass
Pass	Pass		

It has been a dull session so far, and this seems to be a flat hand, but you never know.

West's lead of the ♡9 runs to the 6 and king. South leads the 5 of clubs, West plays the 3 and dummy the jack. As East, how do you plan the defense?

Answer 71

```
                    ♠ Q 8
                    ♡ Q 7 4
                    ◊ A K
                    ♣ A J 10 8 6 4
    ♠ K 7 6 3           N              ♠ J 9 5 2
    ♡ 9 8                              ♡ A J 10 6 3
    ◊ 10 7 6 4      W       E          ◊ Q 5
    ♣ K 9 3            S              ♣ Q 2
                    ♠ A 10 4
                    ♡ K 5 2
                    ◊ J 9 8 3 2
                    ♣ 7 5
```

South plays in 3NT after East has overcalled with one heart. West's lead of the 9 of hearts runs to the 6 and king. At trick two South plays a low club to dummy's jack.

For his free bid of 1 NT South, who appears not to hold the king of clubs, must have the ace of spades. If you win with the queen of clubs and lead a spade, he will go up with the ace and take a second finesse in clubs, making five clubs, two diamonds, one spade and one heart.

But if you hold off the jack of clubs? Then South cannot get the clubs going without letting your partner into the lead. If he crosses to the ace of spades for the next club lead, partner's king of spades becomes an entry.

72. Danger Looms

Dealer West   Neither side vulnerable

$\spadesuit$ 2
$\heartsuit$ 9 8 6 5
$\diamondsuit$ 10 4 3
$\clubsuit$ A K 7 4 3

$\spadesuit$ J 9 5 4 3
$\heartsuit$ 7 2
$\diamondsuit$ Q J 8 6
$\clubsuit$ J 5

South	West	North	East
—	Pass	Pass	1$\spadesuit$
2$\heartsuit$	3$\spadesuit$*	4$\heartsuit$	Pass
Pass	Pass		

* Preemptive in competition

'Do you mind if I watch?' asks a kibitzer, taking a chair beside you at the beginning of the Open Pairs. No, you don't mind. Still, it would be embarrassing if you were to make a mistake on the first deal.

Rejecting experiment, you lead a low spade against four hearts. East wins with the king and returns the 2 of diamonds. Declarer plays the 5 and you win with the jack. What do you play now?

Answer 72

```
              ♠ 2
              ♡ 9 8 6 5
              ◇ 10 4 3
              ♣ A K 7 4 3

♠ J 9 5 4 3        ┌─────────┐        ♠ A K 10 8 6
♡ 7 2              │    N    │        ♡ 10 3
◇ Q J 8 6          │  W   E  │        ◇ K 7 2
♣ J 5             │    S    │        ♣ Q 9 6
                   └─────────┘

              ♠ Q 7
              ♡ A K Q J 4
              ◇ A 9 5
              ♣ 10 8 2
```

South plays in four hearts after East has opened one spade. East wins the spade lead and returns the 2 of diamonds to West's jack.

Where will four tricks come from? One in spades and you must hope for two in diamonds. You need to find partner with one other trick—possibly the ace of hearts, possibly Q x x in clubs.

Certainly you must return a diamond so that you can establish your second trick in this suit before partner's additional winner has been knocked out. However, a danger looms. Suppose you return a low diamond. As the cards lie, declarer can win, draw trumps, ruff a spade, cash the ♣A K, and exit with a diamond, leaving you on play. To prevent this, you must lead back the queen of diamonds.

If you defend this hand correctly, and make sure by some casual remark that your play is understood, you may keep your kibitzer for the rest of the session.

73. Telling Blow

Dealer South   Both sides vulnerable

♠ 9 6 4
♡ Q 9 8 4
◇ Q 6 2
♣ A 9 5

♠ A K 8 3
♡ 7 3
◇ K 8 5 4 3
♣ 10 8

South	West	North	East
—	—	—	—
1♣	Pass	1NT	Pass
3♡	Pass	4♡	Pass
4NT	Pass	5◇	Pass
6♡	Pass	Pass	Pass

You are engaged in a long rubber, which you can scarcely afford to lose, because the opponents already have a small mountain above the line. You lead the king of spades, partner plays the 2 and declarer the queen, which you must read as a singleton. How will you administer a telling blow to the declarer's hopes of a big rubber?

Answer 73

	♠ 9 6 4	
	♡ Q 9 8 4	
	◇ Q 6 2	
	♣ A 9 5	

♠ A K 8 3		♠ J 10 7 5 2
♡ 7 3	N	♡ 10 6 5
◇ K 8 5 4 3	W E	◇ J 9
♣ 10 8	S	♣ 7 4 2

	♠ Q	
	♡ A K J 2	
	◇ A 10 7	
	♣ K Q J 6 3	

South, who has opened one club, plays in six hearts. West wins the first trick with the king of spades and can read South for a singleton.

At the table West led a second spade. South ruffed and drew two top trumps. It struck him that if he drew a third trump he would be a trick short. Breathing hard, he led a low club and finessed the 9. Then he ruffed a third spade with ♡J, crossed to ♣A to draw the last trump, and easily made the rest.

West should conclude, after the first trick, that South has eleven probable tricks by way of four trumps, five clubs, ace of diamonds and one ruff. It is essential to prevent him from reversing the dummy by taking two ruffs in the closed hand. The danger of leading a trump is that you will establish an extra entry to dummy when East holds J x x or 10 x x of hearts. The right play, therefore, is a club-the suit that declarer will need for communication. He may win with ♣9 and ruff a spade, but he cannot contrive to enter dummy, ruff the last spade, and cross again to draw the outstanding trump.

74. Miss By Benito

Dealer South   Neither side vulnerable

♠ K Q J 10 8
♡ Q 4
◇ 8
♣ A K 10 9 2

♣ 6 led   ♠ A 6 5 4
♡ A K 2
◇ Q 9 4
♣ Q J 4

South	West	North	East
2♡	Pass	2♠	Pass
3◇	Pass	4♡	Pass
Pass	Pass		

You have a chance here to outshine Benito Garozzo, who held the East cards, playing against Australia in the qualifying round of the 1979 Bermuda Bowl. South opens with a weak two hearts, North's two spades is forcing, and South's three diamonds indicates strength, and possibly length, in this suit.

West leads the 6 of clubs, dummy wins and South drops the 8. The king of spades is led from dummy. You play the ace, declarer the 2 and West the 9, presumably from a doubleton. How do you plan the defense?

Answer 74

```
              ♠ K Q J 10 8
              ♡ Q 4
              ◇ 8
              ♣ A K 10 9 2

   ♠ 9 3           N          ♠ A 6 5 4
   ♡ 7 3        W     E       ♡ A K 2
   ◇ K 10 7 6 3    S          ◇ Q 9 4
   ♣ 7 6 5 3                  ♣ Q J 4

              ♠ 7 2
              ♡ J 10 9 8 6 5
              ◇ A J 5 2
              ♣ 8
```

South, who has opened a weak two hearts and has rebid in diamonds, plays in four hearts. The club lead is won in dummy and you capture the next trick with the ace of spades. What next?

Garozzo returned a club. South was able then to discard a diamond, ruff two diamonds, and lose only to the top trumps, so making four hearts.

Once declarer plays a spade. a difficult, but logical, defense beats the contract. When in with ace of spades East must play one top heart and then switch to a diamond. Declarer can ruff one diamond and throw one on the king of clubs, but has no way to dispose safely of his last diamond. If he plays another round of trumps, East will cash the diamond queen, and if he attempts to take a discard on the third round of spades, West will ruff. However, as the cards lie, declarer could have made sure of his contract by taking two diamond ruffs and a discard before leading a spade.

75. Hit by Benito

Dealer South   Neither side vulnerable

♠ Q J 7 3 2
♡ J 10 2
◇ A Q 8
♣ K J

♣ 2 led

♠ K 10 9 6 5
♡ A 5
◇ 9 6 5
♣ 8 5 3

South	West	North	East
South	*West*	*North*	*East*
1◇	Pass	1♠	Pass
1NT	Pass	3NT	Pass
Pass			

South's 1 NT rebid is consistent with a minimum opening.

West leads the 2 of clubs (3rd or 5th best). Declarer plays the king from dummy and the 9 from hand. He crosses to the ace of spades, plays a diamond to the ace, and leads the queen of spades from dummy, discarding a low heart. You are in with the king of spades. What do you play now?

Answer 75

```
              ♠ Q J 7 3 2
              ♡ J 10 2
              ◇ A Q 8
              ♣ K J

  ♠ 8 4                            ♠ K 10 9 6 5
  ♡ Q 8 7 3                        ♡ A 5
  ◇ 10 4                           ◇ 9 6 5
  ♣ A 7 6 4 2                      ♣ 8 5 3

              ♠ A
              ♡ K 9 6 4
              ◇ K J 7 3 2
              ♣ Q 10 9
```

Followers of the tournament world may recognize this deal from the 1979 World Championship final between Italy and North America.

Both teams played in 3NT after South had opened one diamond. The Italian declarer won the club lead and ran the jack of hearts; then a low club left South with only eight tricks.

The American declarer at the other table followed a stronger line. He won with the king of clubs, cashed the ace of spades, and crossed to the ace of diamonds to lead the queen of spades, establishing a ninth trick. East won and South discarded a heart.

Audience and commentators were 'giving' South his contract when Garozzo, in with the king of spades, exited with a *diamond*. You see the effect of this? If South cashes the jack of spades, he sets up five tricks for the defense. If he wins in dummy and leads a second club, West can clear the suit and declarer will be cut off from the jack of spades.

South can succeed as the cards lie by winning the second round of diamonds with the jack and leading the 10 of clubs; but that has no bearing on a sparkling play in the field of communication.